Batman: Haunted Knight

The Legends of the Dark Knight Halloween Specials

Three Tales of Halloween in Gotham City

JEPH LOEB & TIM SALE
storytellers

GREGORY WRIGHT
colorist

TODD KLEIN
letterer

ANDROID IMAGES
separations (chapters two and three)

...ated by BOB KANE

BATMAN:
HAUNTED KNIGHT
ISBN 1 85286 739 6

Published by Titan Books Ltd, 42 - 44 Dolben St, London SE1 0UP by arrangement with DC Comics.

Originally published in single magazine form as BATMAN: LEGENDS OF THE DARK KNIGHT HALLOWEEN SPECIAL #1, BATMAN: MADNESS A LEGENDS OF THE DARK KNIGHT HALLOWEEN SPECIAL, and BATMAN: GHOSTS LEGENDS OF THE DARK KNIGHT HALLOWEEN SPECIAL.

Printed in Canada
10 9 8 7 6 5 4 3 2 1

First Edition: November 1996

Cover illustration by Tim Sale
Cover color art by Gregory Wright
Separations by Heroic Age

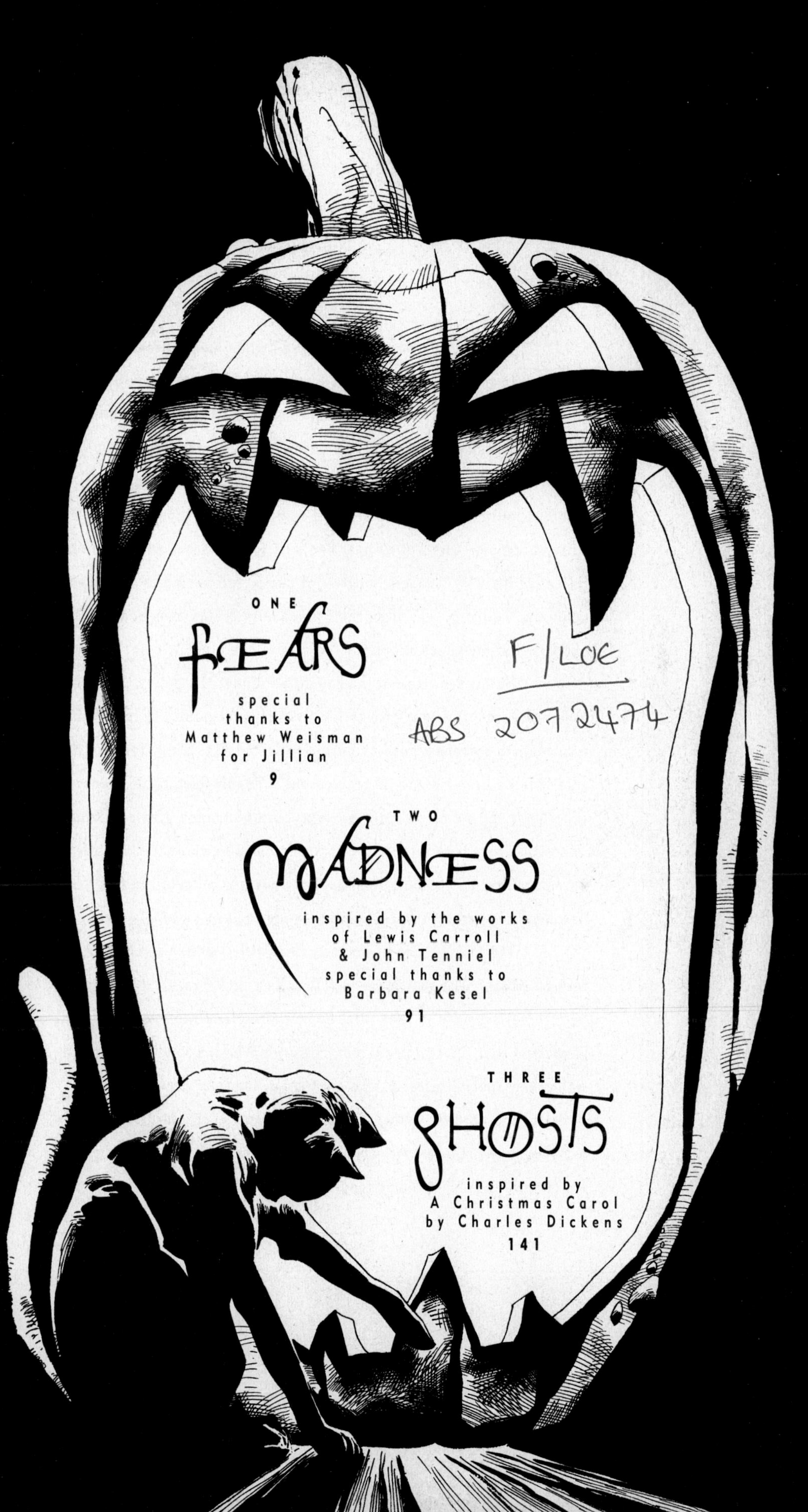
ONE
fEARS
special thanks to Matthew Weisman for Jillian
9
TWO
MADNESS
inspired by the works of Lewis Carroll & John Tenniel
special thanks to Barbara Kesel
91
THREE
GHOSTS
inspired by A Christmas Carol by Charles Dickens
141

Introduction

Trick or Treat

One Halloween night in 1944 when I was seven years old, I hammered the front door of a house on my block and in my best goblin voice yelled "Trick or treat." Suddenly the door flew open and an apparent madman was waving a rifle in my face, screaming he was going to shoot me for trespassing. Too frightened to run, I burst into tears. The madman looked startled. He stopped screaming and showed me that the rifle was empty. This was all just his little joke to scare trick-or-treaters. He called his wife. Large quantities of candy and apologies were heaped upon me. I walked away from their porch with drying eyes and rich in goodies. But my knees shook for the rest of the night.

Halloween. Harmless enough, yet under the giggly thrill of pretend scares, it seems also to have the sinister potential to somehow turn real, to somehow push us onto a rollercoaster ride of fears and emotions we aren't prepared to face but suddenly have to. A queasy experience for me as a seven-year-old, but one loaded with possibilities when you apply it to an already dark and complex character like the Batman. Three of the best such applications are collected in this volume. They are written by Jeph Loeb and illustrated by Tim Sale.

The stories spin out of a Batman title I edit, LEGENDS OF THE DARK KNIGHT. The first story in this collection, "Fears," was going to be a three-issue arc in that title. Somewhere along the line, Jeph suggested that, given the subject matter, maybe it could be a Batman Halloween Special instead. Like most great ideas, it seemed simple, obvious, and natural. Amazingly, given Batman's "creature of the night" persona, no one in recent memory had tried anything quite like it. Best of all, the material was more than strong enough to support the special format.

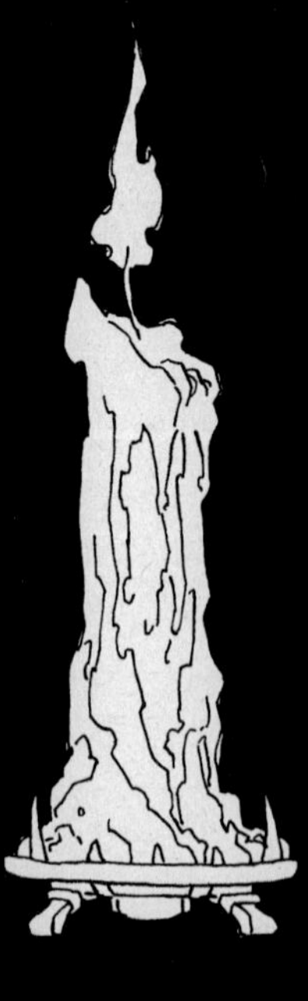

Set in the early years of Batman's career, LEGENDS OF THE DARK KNIGHT story arcs function like self-contained novels or novelettes without the ongoing continuity associated with most comics today. To avoid seeming like mechanical set pieces, they have to have unique style, point of view and emotional depth, revealing new aspects of the Dark Knight, his friends, his foes, his city. It's a challenge not everyone can rise to, but one Jeph and Tim obviously thrive on.

Working together seems to bring out the best in them. Working together on Batman seems to bring out even better than that. They immerse themselves totally in the material, bringing to it not only their love of the character, but of comics and movies and genre fiction in general. They worry over everything from the change of a word to the choice of a color. They lobby long and hard to make sure anything not done by themselves is done by the best in the field, such as letterer Todd Klein and colorist Gregory Wright. Obsessive? Sure, but all in service of the story they're telling. And, as you'll see when you read this collection, there's a trick to doing a great Batman Halloween story. The trick is that it has to be a great Batman story first. The treat is that Jeph and Tim have mastered the trick.

The first LEGENDS OF THE DARK KNIGHT HALLOWEEN SPECIAL sold out within weeks of its first appearance. That was going to be it. A one-time thing. Then Jeph and Tim had some thoughts about Alice in Wonderland that grew into "Madness." And that was going to be it, except that they had another thought about Charles Dickens and suddenly there was "Ghosts." From one story somehow a tradition evolved. Is the tradition over? Well, it was going to be with this collection. Except Jeph and Tim had this idea not for just a special, but a special *series* involving a year in Batman's life, a year that covers thirteen months. It's called THE LONG HALLOWEEN. They're already under way with it. As an editor, I'm excited, but...the seven-year-old in me finds his knees begin to shake.

—Archie Goodwin

TS

FEARS

ONE

In Los Angeles at this time of year, everyone with a gun fires it into the air. People are killed from the falling bullets.
In Cincinnati a curfew prevents the children from "trick or treating" after dark.
In Detroit they call it "Devil's Night." Buildings are torched. Fires sweep throughout the city unchecked.
But, in Gotham City, on Halloween...

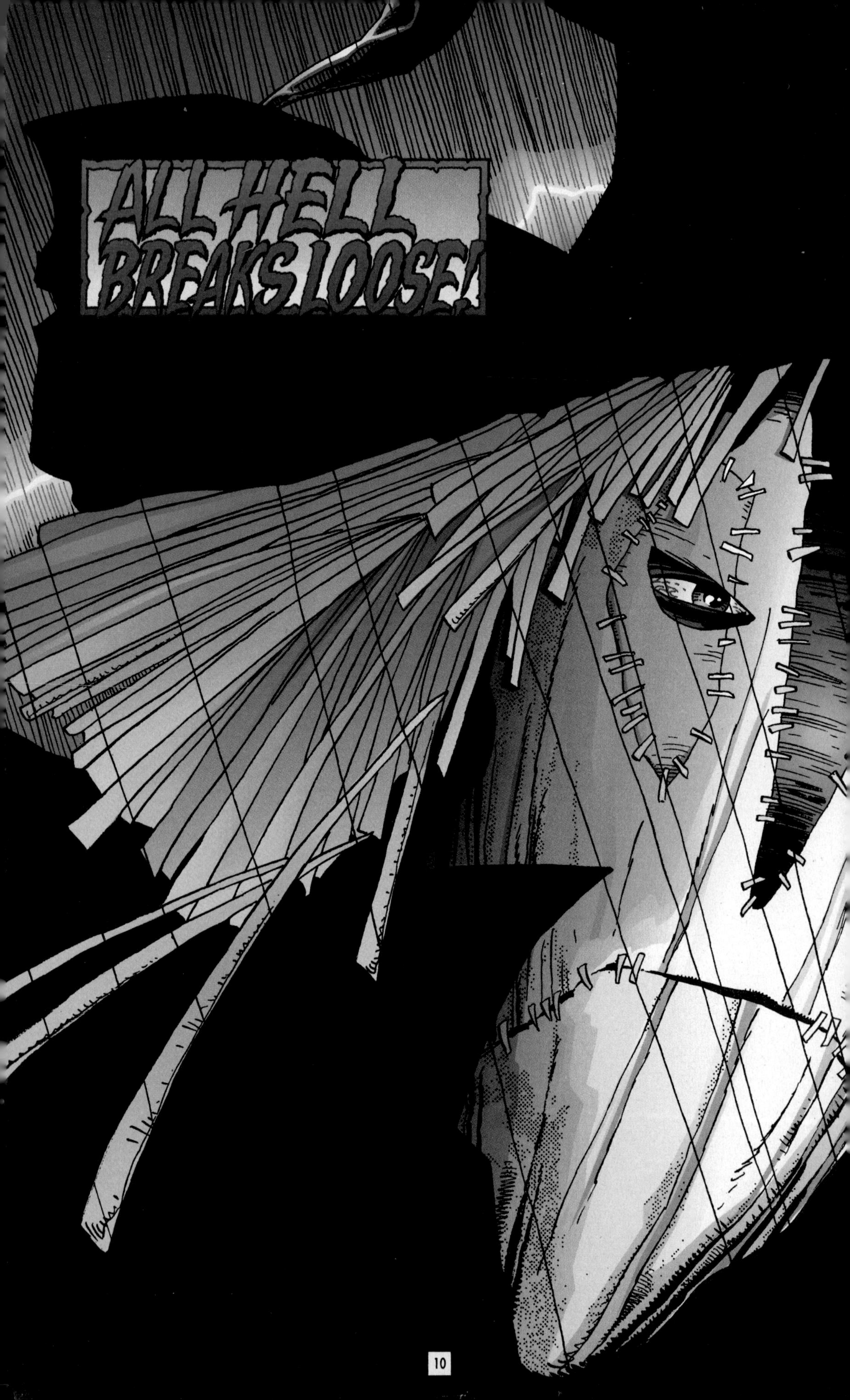
ALL HELL BREAKS LOOSE!

He calls himself "Scarecrow." Psychologist turned psychopath. He preys on the innocent and instills them with fear.
When I chose to wear my... costume, it was to prey upon the criminals, and instill them with fear.
The irony is not lost on me...

WHEN YOU THINK J.C.'S GONNA CALL, MATT?
WHEN HE'S GOOD AND READY, STANLEY.
JUST LIKE EVERY OTHER NIGHT THIS WEEK.
HEY! WHO TURNED OUT THE LIGHTS?
WHOEVER HE IS JUST BOUGHT A HEAP OF TROUBLE.
SAM, COVER THE FRONT DOOR. SIMON, YOU--
I'M ONLY GOING TO ASK YOU ONCE.

WHERE IS JONATHAN CRANE?
IT'S--THE B-BATMAN!
THERE'S FOUR OF US! LET'S TAKE HIM!

YOU CAN'T RUN...

YOU CAN'T HIDE...

I KNOW WHO YOU'VE BEEN WORKING FOR...

TELL ME.
WHERE IS JONATHAN CRANE?
WHERE IS SCARECROW?
I CAN'T...
I DON'T KNOW...
I...AAAAAHHHHHH

He calls himself "Scarecrow."
For nearly a week he has been blowing up Gotham Electric relay stations.
Knocking out power in select portions of the city. Plunging them into darkness.
And while the innocent grope around in the dark...
...he and his men have been looting Gotham City.
Tonight... that...all... ends!

SCARECROW!
KNICK KNACK PADDY WHACK GIVE THE DOG A BONE.
I'M NOT AFRAID OF YOU, YOU KNOW.
YOU SHOULD BE AFRAID.
VERY AFRAID.

Tired.
Haven't slept in several days.
CRANE!
I'M TAKING YOU BACK TO YOUR PADDED CELL!
HELLO.
GOOD-BYE.
BEEN THERE.
DONE THAT.

Endless hours of detective work...all comes down to this.
One man running away. While another man pursues him.
Why are the... disturbed ones always the most elusive?
PEOPLE SAY I'M CRAZY.
YOU DON'T HAVE THE SENSE TO COME IN OUT OF THE RAIN--
--AND I DO.
GOTHAM ELECTRIC
YOU NEED HELP. MEDICAL HELP.
DON'T MAKE THIS...
...DIFFICULT.
THAT WAY IS A VERY NICE WAY.
IT'S PLEASANT DOWN THIS WAY, TOO.
OF COURSE, PEOPLE DO GO BOTH WAYS.

BIG SCARY BAT MAN. WHAT SCARES YOU?
LET'S FIND OUT.
THIS NEW TOXIN IS PARTICULARLY EFFECTIVE.
SO... I TRIPLED THE DOSE!
NOW, THIS SHOULDN'T TAKE MUCH MORE THAN A --
"BOO!"
OH... MY...
SHUT UP.

BOTH OF YOU, FREEZE! PUT YOUR HANDS WHERE I CAN SEE--
OH. IT'S YOU.
I ALREADY KNOW THE ANSWER, BUT--DO YOU NEED ANY HELP?
WHO DO YOU HAVE THERE--CRANE? HOW MANY TIMES DOES THIS MAKE IT?
GET THAT LIGHT OUT OF MY EYES!

GOTHAM ELECTRIC

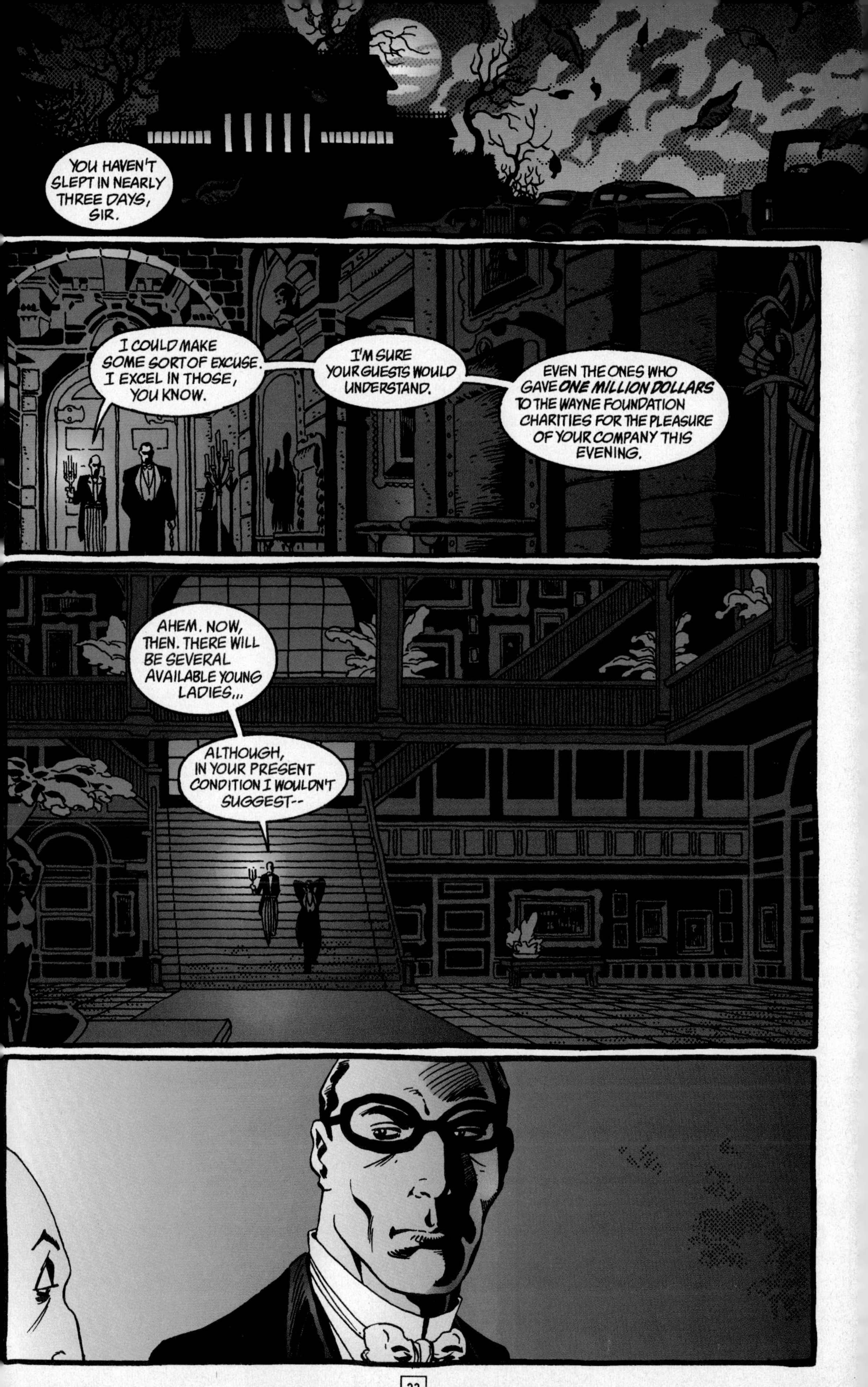

YOU HAVEN'T SLEPT IN NEARLY THREE DAYS, SIR.

I COULD MAKE SOME SORT OF EXCUSE. I EXCEL IN THOSE, YOU KNOW.

I'M SURE YOUR GUESTS WOULD UNDERSTAND.

EVEN THE ONES WHO GAVE **ONE MILLION DOLLARS** TO THE WAYNE FOUNDATION CHARITIES FOR THE PLEASURE OF YOUR COMPANY THIS EVENING.

There are certain advantages to maintaining the guise of Bruce Wayne, millionaire playboy.
Mingling with Gotham City's elite-- the wealthy-- the powerful-- the perverse--
Keeps me abreast of what is happening in my city.
Although I'm very rarely told something I don't already know.
I cannot afford to be surprised.
51
51

GOTHAM ELECTRIC SEEMS TO BE IN TROUBLE, BRUCE. THINK THEY WANT TO SELL?
HOISCH, BY THE TIME I KNOW, YOU'LL KNOW!

WAYNE--
JIM! GOOD OF YOU TO MAKE IT.
BARBARA HAVING A GOOD TIME?

YES, I SUPPOSE... THOUGHT I SAW HER PLAYING POOL WITH HARRISON FORD.
HE'S A DELIGHT-- WHOA!

DO YOU DANCE, MR. WAYNE?
I... don't know this woman...

POLICE
KNICK KNACK PADDY WHACK GIVE A DOG A BONE.
ZIP IT, CRANE.
OR WE'LL ZIP IT FOR YOU.
I KNOW A MAN WHO HAD A DOG.
PLNK
SSSSSSSS
HIS DOG TOLD HIM TO CUT HIS ENTIRE FAMILY INTO PIECES.
BARK.
BARK.
BARK.
BARK!
BARK!
NO... DON'T...!
POLICE
WATCH OUT... AAAAAAH!
NO

I CAN SEE YOU SPARED NO EXPENSE ON YOUR OUTFIT.
I'M... NOT MUCH FOR COSTUMES.
I DON'T KNOW YOU. DO I?
OF COURSE NOT. I'M IN DISGUISE.
DISGUISE?
YES. I DON'T USUALLY WEAR...
KRASH!
...GLASSES.
THAT WOULD BE MY DOGS...

HOTSPUR!
DAISY!
MR. WAYNE, I'LL PAY FOR ALL THE DAMAGE--
PERHAPS I CAN BE OF SERVICE.
THERE IS A LIGHT IN THE SKY, SIR...
...I ASSUME YOU WILL BE EXITING.
WHAT IS IT ABOUT THIS OLD CLOCK THAT WOULD GET YOU TWO SO RILED UP?
I AM NOT MISTAKEN, AM I, SIR?
YOU WILL BE WEARING A COSTUME THIS EVENING AFTER ALL...?
GET HER NUMBER, ALFRED.
I CAN THINK OF NOTHING I'D RATHER DO.
AND HOW MIGHT WE GET IN TOUCH WITH YOU, MISS...?
DON'T WORRY. I'LL BE IN TOUCH...

He calls himself "Scarecrow." In the time it has taken me to respond, he has blown up another relay station.
Half the city is without power. Seems like the other half is stricken with fires and looting.
Tired... I want to go to bed... I don't really have a choice...
Gotham City. She chose me...

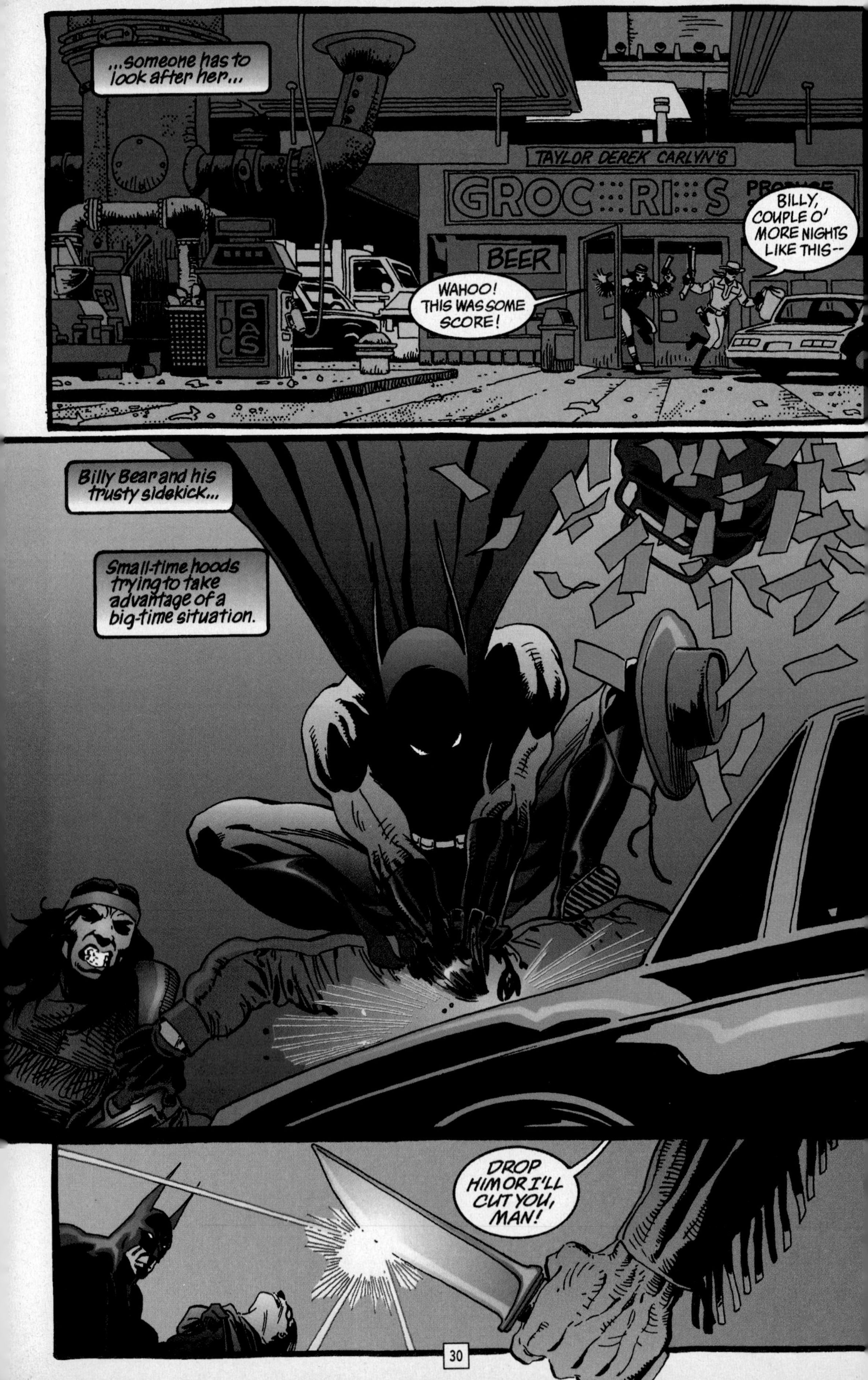

...someone has to look after her...

TAYLOR DEREK CARLYN'S

GROC RI S

BEER

WAHOO! THIS WAS SOME SCORE!

BILLY, COUPLE O' MORE NIGHTS LIKE THIS--

Billy Bear and his trusty sidekick...

Small-time hoods trying to take advantage of a big-time situation.

HA! CUT YOU! NOT SO TOUGH, ARE YOU, BATMAN?
. . .
TOUGH ENOUGH.
He... cut me... like I was some... amateur...
Maybe... I'm more tired than I thought...

Earlier tonight, I apprehended Scarecrow. Somehow... Gordon and his men allowed him to escape.
Despite my efforts... Scarecrow is still out there.

I had a party for the Wayne Foundation I didn't want to have.
I had to leave the party when I didn't want to.

I met a woman who...
I don't even know her name...
...tired...
INC

PARTY ENDED ABOUT AN HOUR AGO, SIR. EVERYONE HAD A WONDERFUL TIME. THEY ALL ASSUMED YOU WERE UPSTAIRS... ENTERTAINING.
BRING ME SOME TEA, ALFRED. AND A JELLY DOUGHNUT.
OH? YOU'RE NOT PLANNING ON EATING ONE, ARE YOU, SIR?
Knick knack. Paddy whack. Give a dog a bone.
...where is Scarecrow?

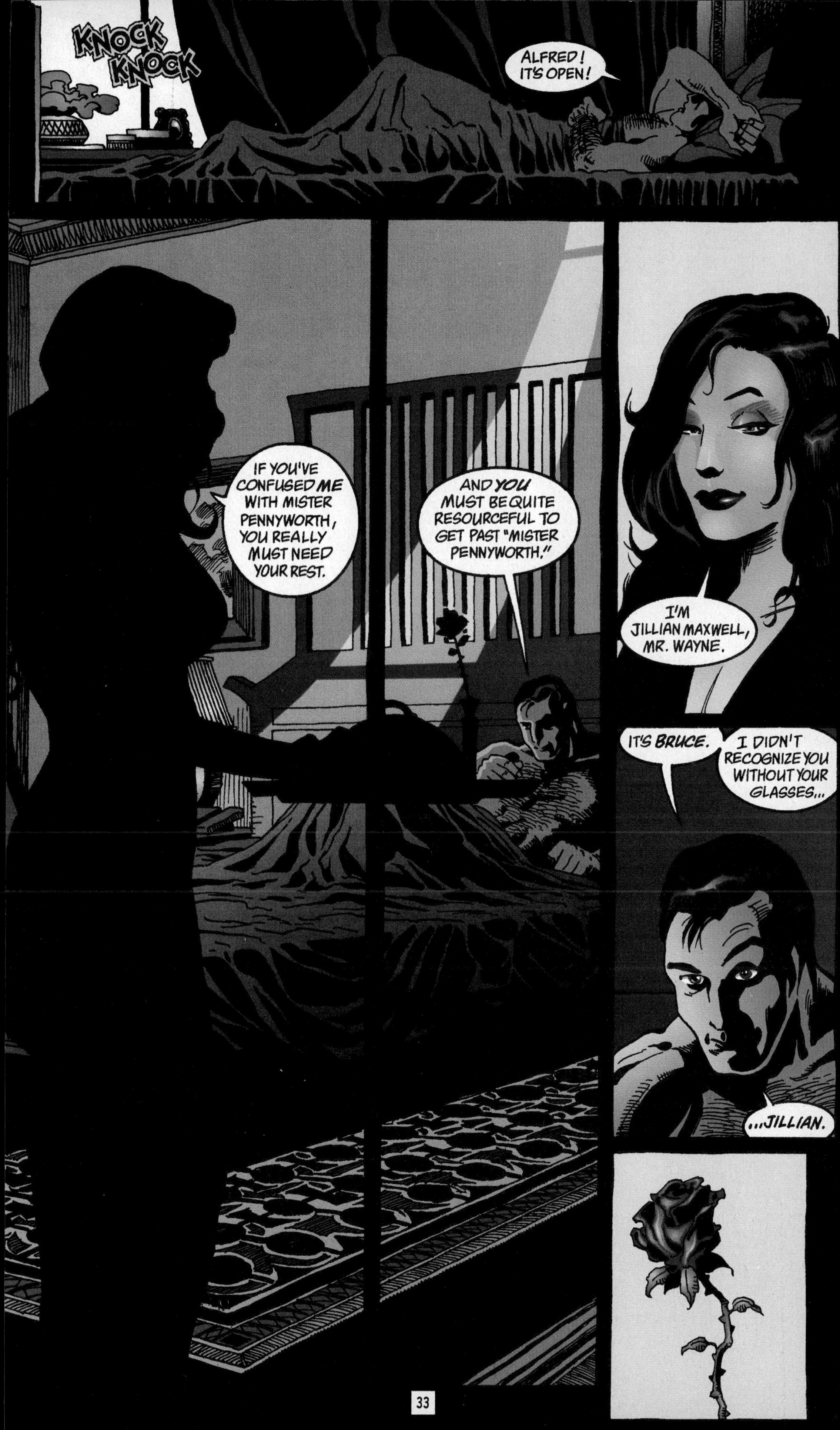

KNOCK KNOCK

ALFRED! IT'S OPEN!

II
TS

"I have to go to work..."
"Who works on a Saturday night?"
"Money never sleeps," I told her. If I were honest about it, I would've said...
"Crime never sleeps"...

It's odd... that on a night like this... I remember my father...
The phone would ring. There was a medical emergency somewhere.
He had to go. He was needed. There was no choice.
Is that why I'm here...?

The second night of the Halloween weekend and Scarecrow is loose in my city.
Waiting...for him to show himself...knowing when he does...innocent people will be hurt.
Waiting for the crime...
"Stay..."
"Go..."
"Stay..."
Remembering Jillian... What is it she said...?
"Did you ever have the feeling that you wanted to go? Did you ever have the feeling that you wanted to stay..."

Bats...?

No... crows!

Scarecrow uses a fear toxin.
It chemically alters behavior.
Previously, his experiments were limited to humans.
This is...new...

Arm has gone numb. Cracked at least two ribs.

"Bruce... for a man who could have anything he wanted...

"...why do I have the sense that you rarely get what you want?"

It's odd... that at a time like this... I'm remembering...

...JILLIAN.
THE...PARTY WAS EXHAUSTING. I THOUGHT I'D GET SOME SLEEP.
NO GOOD DEED GOES UNPUNISHED.
YOUNG LADY!
MY APOLOGIES, MASTER BRUCE. I SET YOUR TEA SERVING DOWN FOR ONLY A MOMENT--
--AND THE NEXT THING YOU KNEW--
--MISS MAXWELL WAS IN MY BEDROOM.
THIS SORT OF THING MUST HAPPEN A LOT TO YOU MILLIONAIRE PLAYBOYS.
WE'RE UPSETTING MR. PENNYWORTH, BRUCE.
TELL YOU WHAT. WHY DON'T WE ADJOURN...

"...TO THE PATIO."
TELL ME SOMETHING ABOUT YOURSELF, JILLIAN.
BRUCE. WERE YOU EVER BIT BY A DEAD BEE?
WHAT? NO. A DEAD BEE IS A...
...DEAD BEE.
WHAT ABOUT YOU, MR. PENNYWORTH?
YES, MISS, I WAS. QUITE PAINFUL, ACTUALLY.
WHAT DID YOU DO?
I BIT HIM BACK.
YOU... BIT HIM BACK?
YOU'RE ALL RIGHT, ALFRED. I CAN SEE WHY BRUCE KEEPS YOU AROUND.
YES, MISS.

Jillian wants to go for a ride.. And I'm beginning to suspect--
--what Jillian wants... Jillian gets.
WHAT WAS ALL THAT ABOUT A DEAD BEE?
MISS JILLIAN APPARENTLY HAS A UNIQUE SENSE OF HUMOR--
--AS WELL AS A LOVE FOR OLD FILM DIALOGUE.
THE BUS IS LEAVING!
THEN, YOU TWO SHOULD GET ALONG FAMOUSLY.
IF I MAY SAY SO, SIR, IT'S NOT ME WHO HAS TO GET ALONG WITH HER.
THERE'S... SOMETHING SPECIAL ABOUT THIS ONE, ALFRED.

Tiffany's. Bloomingdale's. The Frick. And now, this.
JILLIAN! I'VE LIVED IN GOTHAM CITY FOR YEARS AND I'VE NEVER TAKEN ONE OF THESE RIDES.
Her energy is... boundless.
Why do I feel so... free?
WHAT A LOVELY DAY TO TRY SOMETHING NEW.
POLITICS?
NOT... INTENTIONALLY. I FIND IT... TIME-CONSUMING.
TRAVEL?
NOT... AS MUCH AS I LIKE TO.
THEATER?
I'VE MISSED A LOT. I'M... OFTEN BUSY AT NIGHT.
MUSIC?
I TRY TO KEEP UP WITH... UM...
WHAT KIND OF MUSIC DO YOU LIKE?
MR. WAYNE, ARE YOU INVOLVED WITH ANYONE RIGHT NOW?
I... HAVE A NUMBER OF OBLIGATIONS. BUT, NONE OF THEM ARE ROMANTIC.
BRUCE... FOR A MAN WHO COULD HAVE ANYTHING HE WANTED...
WHY DO I HAVE THE SENSE THAT YOU RARELY GET WHAT YOU WANT?
An innocent question...

...answered by my reality.
I'M ONLY GONNA ASK YOUSE ONCE.
GIMME THE LADY'S PURSE.
DON'T!
DON'T BE NO HERO, BUB!
SORRY, FOLKS. I'LL...GO CALL THE COPS.
SEE, THE POLICE WILL HANDLE IT.
BRUCE, IT'S ONLY MONEY.
IT'S NOT WORTH YOUR LIFE.

Night is coming. I have to go to work.
A LOVELY RIDE AND A HOLD-UP.
YOU CERTAINLY KNOW HOW TO SHOW A GIRL A GOOD TIME.
AS MUCH AS I HATE FOR IT TO END...I HAVE TO GO TO WORK.
WHO WORKS ON A SATURDAY NIGHT?
MONEY NEVER SLEEPS.
DID YOU EVER HAVE THE FEELING THAT YOU WANTED TO GO? DID YOU EVER HAVE THE FEELING THAT YOU WANTED TO STAY...
"Stay..."
"Go..."
"Stay..."
THE POLICE TELEPHONED.
THE POLICE?
SOMETHING ABOUT NABBING A THIEF AND RECOVERING MISS MAXWELL'S PURSE.
YOU WEREN'T HURT, WERE YOU, SIR?
THE POLICE DID CATCH HIM...
MAYBE... I DON'T HAVE TO WORK TONIGHT...
IF THE CHOICE IS BETWEEN PARADING ABOUT THE CITY IN YOUR LONG JOHNS OR GETTING A GOOD NIGHT'S REST--
Is it too late to catch Jillian?
OH, GOOD SHOW, SIR.
FOR A MOMENT, I WAS AFRAID YOU'D HAD A RATIONAL THOUGHT.
I don't have a choice... Crime never sleeps.
Scarecrow is loose in my city...

I KNOW AN OLD WOMAN...

WHO LIVED IN A SHOE...

SHE HAD SO MANY CHILDREN...

SHE DIDN'T KNOW WHAT TO DO...

SHE GAVE THEM SOME BROTH...

BUT GAVE THEM NO BREAD...

AND SHE BEAT THEM AND WHIPPED THEM AND PUT THEM TO BED.
NOW, MY PRETTY, ONLY ONE QUESTION REMAINS.
DID YOU GET THIS PRIZE--
--WITHOUT BAT MAN FOLLOWING YOU?!

...CRANE...
PROFESSOR CRANE ISSSN'T HEAR RIGHT NOW.
BUT, IF YOU'D LIKE TO MAKE AN APPOINTMENT--?

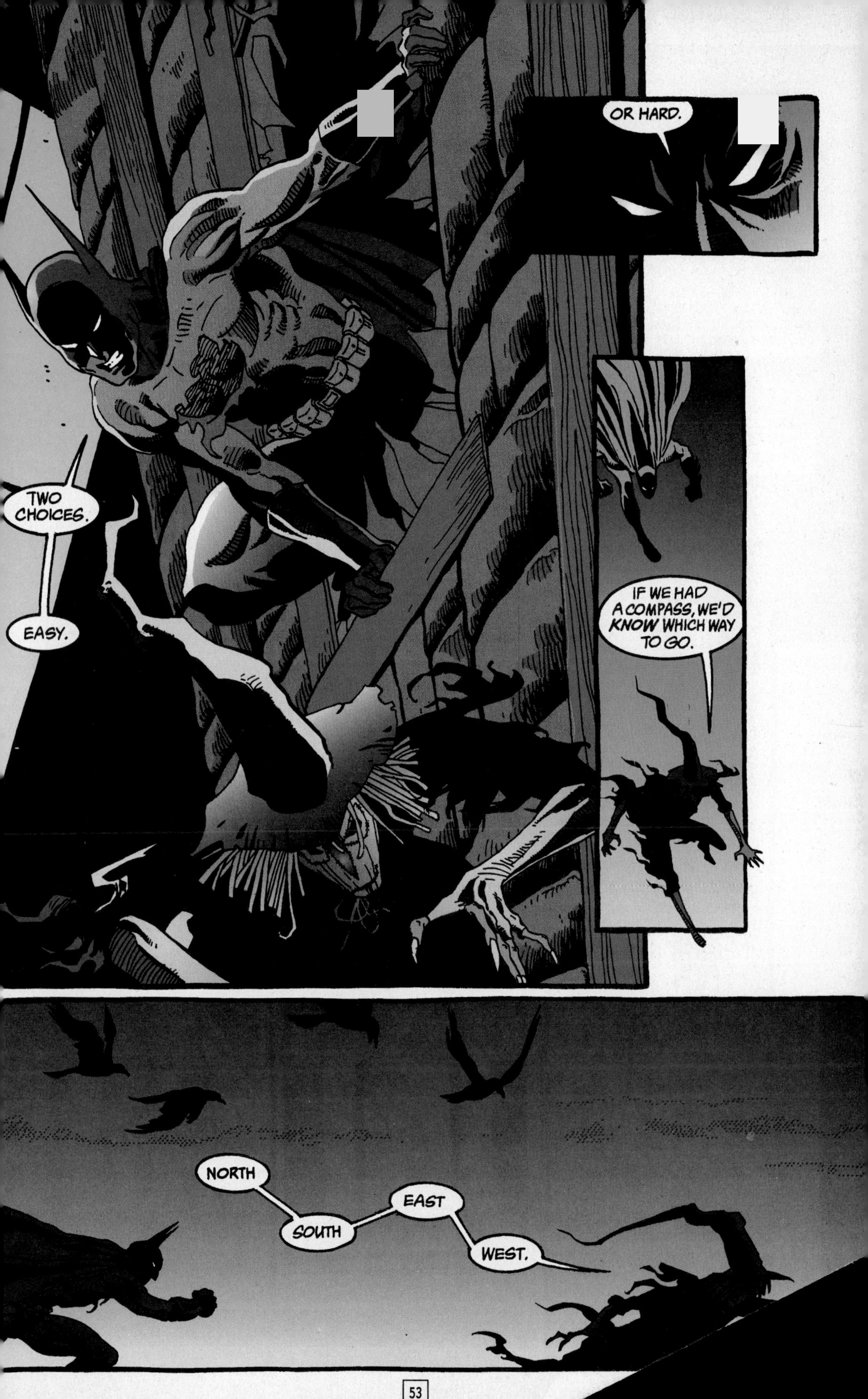

TWO CHOICES.

EASY.

OR HARD.

IF WE HAD A COMPASS, WE'D *KNOW* WHICH WAY TO GO.

The Gotham Central Park Maze. I thought it was closed.
Years ago, two children wandered in. The police searched and searched.
When they found them, it was too late... the children were...
The place should have been burned to the ground...
SEE HOW THEY RUN.
SEE HOW THEY RUN.
SHE CUT OFF THEIR TAILS WITH A CARVING KNIFE!
HAVE YOU EVER SEEN SUCH A SIGHT IN YOUR LIFE?

Around this corner, he's--
...gone...
SEE

HOW
SCARECROW!

THEY
...the thorns...

RUN
...Scarecrow...
...poison...

SEE
HOW
THEY
RUN

MISS MAXWELL. WHAT ARE YOU DOING IN HERE?
BRUCE TOLD ME TO WAIT FOR HIM.
HE LEFT ME NO SUCH INSTRUCTIONS.
AND I'M CERTAIN YOU'LL BE MORE COMFORT-ABLE...ELSEWHERE.
ANYWAY. I HAVE TO RUN.
ALFRED, WHAT THIS OLD PLACE NEEDS IS A WOMAN'S TOUCH. DON'T YOU THINK SO?
THERE IS MORE TO THIS WOMAN THAN MEETS THE EYE.
I WILL HAVE TO DISCUSS THIS WITH MASTER BRUCE...

--WHEN HE GETS HOME...!

I had to go to work tonight...
I think of my father. The phone would ring. He would go.
"No good deed goes unpunished..."

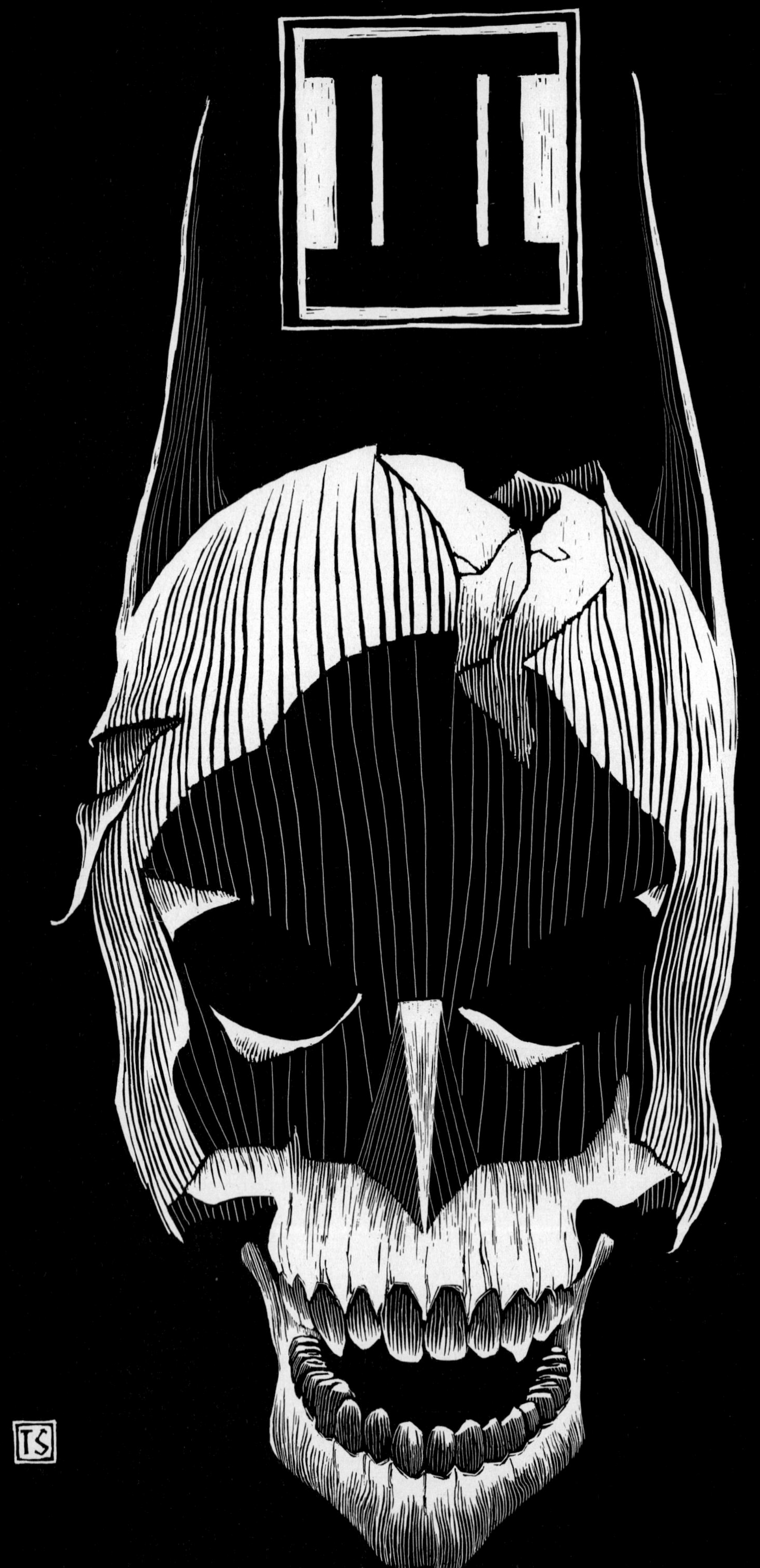
III
TS

ENTER
MOUTH
#2345*%

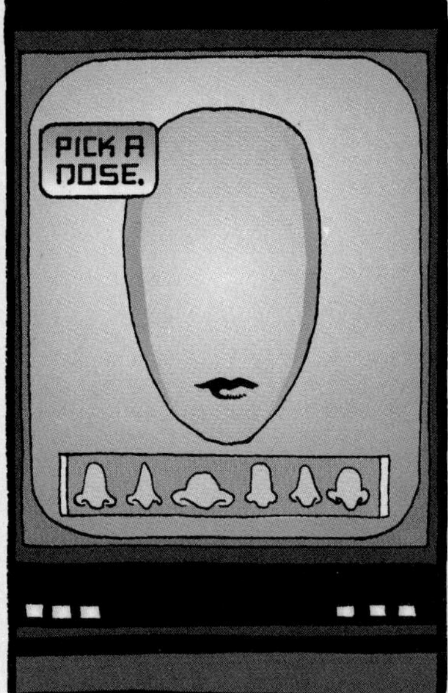
PICK A
NOSE.

SOFTWARE
HUMOR.
HOW...
DROLL.

EYES?

TWO
OUGHT TO DO
NICELY.

SEARCHING...

FBI
CIA
INTERPOL
SCOTLAND
YARD
KGB

DING!
GOOD
LORD.

HE'S
HOME JUST
IN TIME...

I've known him for so very long. Each of us going about our duties— no matter how unpleasant.
Thinking only of the greater good.
I suppose it is one of the few things we have in common.
WE TRUST

MASTER BRUCE.
But tonight, I fear, I have a task which is... most unpleasant...

MASTER BRUCE?
WRRR-KLIK!
MASTER BRUCE!
MASTER BRUCE...

I DON'T KNOW IF YOU CAN HEAR ME.
YOU'RE EXPERIENCING SOME SORT OF TOXIC SHOCK.
I'VE GIVEN YOU AN ANTIDOTE.
AND WHILE I KNOW YOU DON'T THINK MUCH OF PRAYER...
...I MAY HAVE TO RESORT TO THAT.
He calls himself "Scarecrow." He preys on the fears one keeps hidden in his heart.
I remember... chasing him...
...but not... a church?
Why... a church?
DEARLY BELOVED...
...WE ARE GATHERED HERE TODAY...

...not a church...
a maze!
...TO WITNESS THE UNION OF TWO PEOPLE.
A UNION THAT IS A SACRED TRUST.
...thorns...?
Thorns. Maze. Fears.
...why...a church...?

DO YOU, BATMAN, PROMISE--
TO LOVE.
TO HONOR.
TO OBEY.

So. help. you. God.
Thorns. Maze. Fears. Church...
...Jillian.
Jillian.

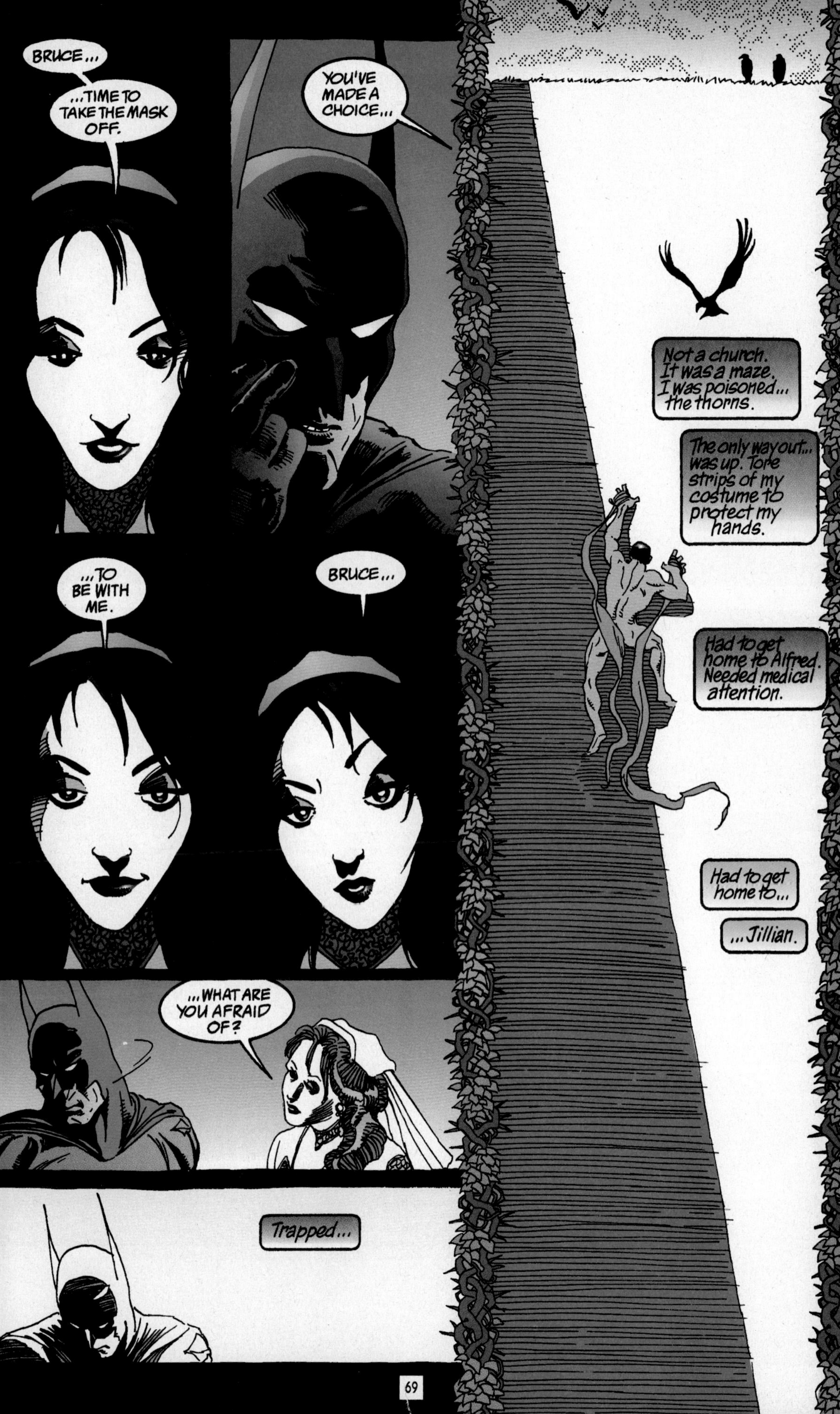
BRUCE...
...TIME TO TAKE THE MASK OFF.
YOU'VE MADE A CHOICE...
...TO BE WITH ME.
BRUCE...
...WHAT ARE YOU AFRAID OF?
Trapped...
Not a church. It was a maze. I was poisoned... the thorns.
The only way out... was up. Tore strips of my costume to protect my hands.
Had to get home to Alfred. Needed medical attention.
Had to get home to...
...Jillian.

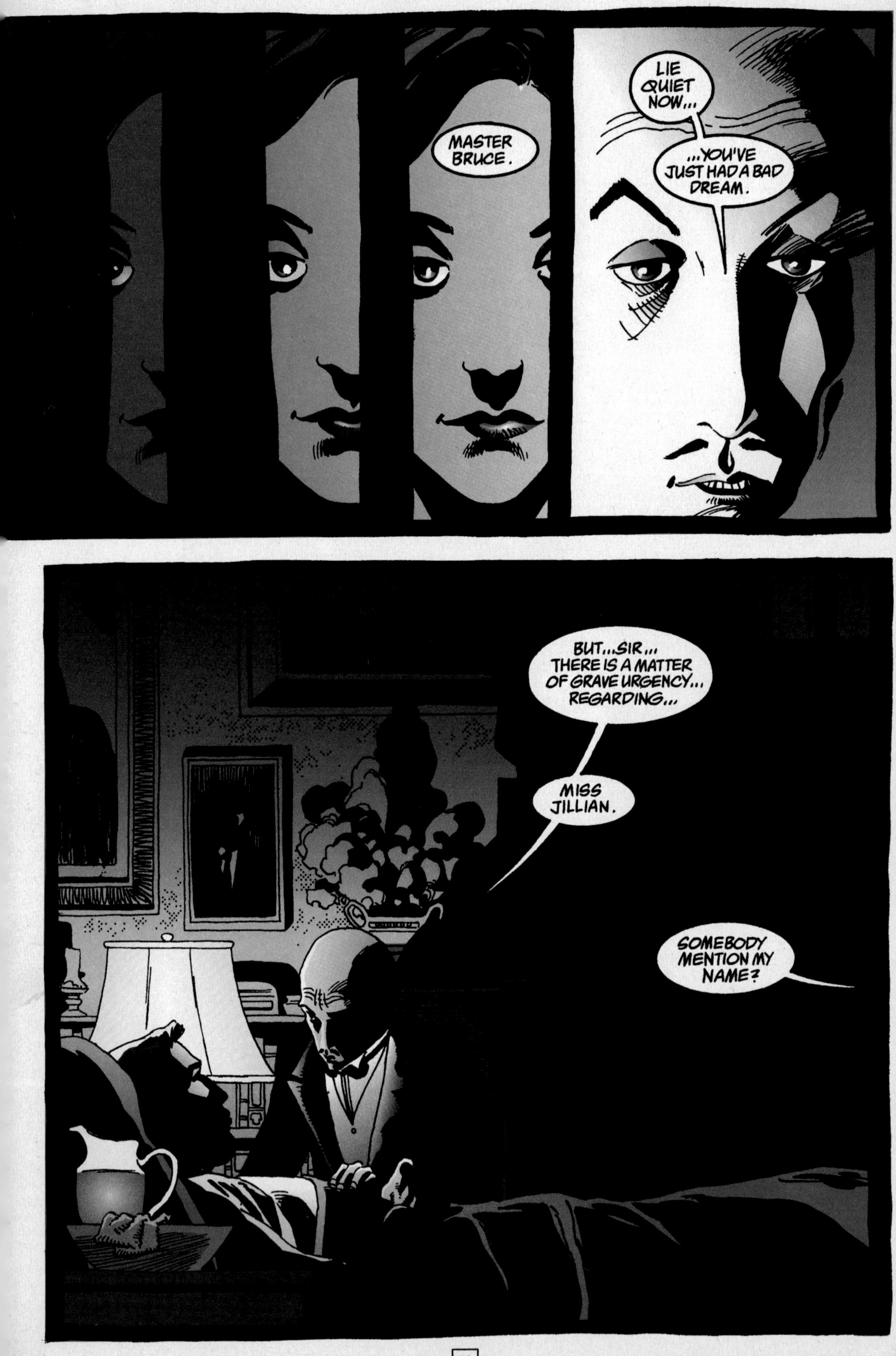

BUT...SIR... THERE IS A MATTER OF GRAVE URGENCY... REGARDING...

MISS JILLIAN.

SOMEBODY MENTION MY NAME?

JILLIAN.
SEEMS I'M ALWAYS FINDING YOU IN BED.
ALFRED, GIVE ME A MOMENT WITH MISS MAXWELL.
ALONE.
...AS YOU WISH, SIR.
YOU LOOK POSITIVELY GREEN AROUND THE GILLS.
AH... FOOD POISONING. I'M FINE, NOW... BUT...
JILLIAN...
I'M THINKING ABOUT TAKING SOME TIME OFF. TO TRAVEL.
WOULD YOU LIKE TO ACCOMPANY ME?
ARE YOU SURE? WHAT ABOUT YOUR... RESPONSIBILITIES?
NO, I'M NOT SURE.
MAYBE THAT'S WHY I HAVE TO DO THIS.

GUESS HE'S NOT COMING...
SHOULD WE SHUT IT OFF?
Scarecrow phoned City Hall.
He's going to kidnap a city official, unless he gets $100,000.
Scared the hell out of every civil servant in Gotham.
I need help.
DON'T WORRY, CAPTAIN.
WE CAN HANDLE IT WITHOUT BATMAN.
I hope you're not lying some-where hurt.
CLICK
I hope you're not... dead.
I sound like some worried father when his son hasn't come home with the family car.
Or is it worse... did you not show up tonight... by choice?
JIM...
I'VE GOT TO BE HONEST.
I WAS BEGINNING TO THINK YOU WEREN'T GOING TO COME.

HICKORY.
DICKORY.
DOC.
YOU!?
THE MOUSE RAN UP THE CLOCK.

THE CLOCK STRUCK ONE.
BEFORE HE COULD RUN.
HICKORY. DICKORY. DOC.

I DON'T THINK YOU'RE QUITE READY TO BE UP AND AROUND.
FOR ONCE, I AGREE WITH YOU.
THAT'S WHY I'D LIKE YOU TO PACK A STEAMER TRUNK FOR ME.
THE... STEAMER...?
AROUND THE WORLD. THE LA PALOMA LEAVES PIER 27 AT MIDNIGHT.
AND JILLIAN AND I WILL BE ON IT.
JILLIAN...?
BEFORE YOU DO THAT, SIR, I'D ASK THAT YOU LOOK AT THIS.
I'M SURE IT CAN WAIT, ALFRED.
I HAD THE COMPUTER CHECK ON MISS JILLIAN MAXWELL.
YOU HAD NO *RIGHT*.
I KNOW, SIR. BUT, WHEN YOU CARE FOR SOMEONE AS I DO YOU...
...I HAD NO *CHOICE*.
I'LL TENDER MY RESIGNATION, IF THAT IS YOUR WISH.

I should throw the disk away without looking at it.
Leap at a chance for happiness.
But... I know what it is like...
...not to have a choice.

CLICK
Not good. No sign of Gordon.
B-B-B-BATMAN...
EASY... EASY NOW.
HE--HE--TOOK--TOOK--TOOK--THE CAPTAIN.
HICK. HICK. HICKORY. DICKORY. DOC.
THE MOUSE... RAN UP...

JACK AND JILL WENT UP THE HILL TO FETCH A PAIL OF WATER.
JACK FELL DOWN. BROKE HIS CROWN.
CRANE. LET'S GO BACK INSIDE.
YOU'VE *WON*. I'LL GET YOU THE RANSOM MONEY.
YOU KNOW, JIM...
THE INTERESTING THING ABOUT A FEAR OF HEIGHTS IS IT'S A VERY *PRACTICAL* FEAR.
WHY, A FALL FROM *THIS* HEIGHT--

HEY!
I WAS TALKING TO JIM HERE--!
THANK GOD, IT'S YOU!
STAY HERE. I'M GOING AFTER CRANE.
I... KNOW. IT'S WHAT YOU DO.
TOM, TOM, THE PIPER'S SON.
STOLE A PIG.
AND AWAY HE--

SCARECROW!
LITTLE BOY BLUE COME BLOW YOUR HORN--
THE SHEEP'S IN THE--
STOP IT! THIS ISN'T A GAME!

He'll never know what he did to me...
...how far inside his poison reached...
...to very private things.
LITTLE MISS MUFFET...
LITTLE JACK HORNER...
THE THREE LITTLE KITTENS!
GO. GOO. GOO. GOOOSSE.
MOTHER.

How tempting it was to ignore the batsignal...
How hard it was to ignore...
my desires...

...private fears I cannot quell... or change...
Once Scarecrow touched those fears...
...he never had a chance.

ALFRED! BE A SPORT AND LUG MY LUGGAGE UP FROM THE CAR.
NO, MISS MAXWELL--
--OR SHOULD I SAY, MRS. KATHRYN COLE?
OR MRS. CHRISTINE GHERARD. OR MRS. DIANA LOPEZ. OR MRS. PAMELA WEISMAN.
YOU HAVE BEEN, AT ONE TIME OR ANOTHER, ALL OF THOSE WOMEN.
ALWAYS A RICH HUSBAND.
ALL OF WHOM DIED... ACCIDENTALLY.
SO, YOU WON'T MIND IF I DO YOU THE FAVOR OF NOT LETTING MR. WAYNE...
...MAKE YOU A WIDOW AGAIN.
SLAP!
BRUCE WILL HEAR ABOUT THIS.
YES, MISS. I AM CERTAIN THAT HE WILL.

I DON'T PRETEND TO BE AN EXPERT ON THE HUMAN HEART...
...BUT, I SUSPECT THAT LEARNING THE TRUTH ABOUT... JILLIAN... MUST BE VERY DIFFI-CULT FOR YOU.
WONDERING HOW SUCH A GREAT DETEC-TIVE COULD HAVE MADE SO GREAT A MISTAKE.
I OFFER YOU THIS THOUGHT.
PERHAPS IT WASN'T BATMAN WHO MADE THE ERROR...
... BUT ONLY BRUCE WAYNE.
ERASE...
ERASE...
ERASE...
ERASE...
ERASE...
ERASE...
ERASE...

I learned something over this Halloween weekend.
I thought that I didn't have a choice about being the Batman.
That Gotham City chose me to protect her.
That is wrong.
Ever since the night my parents were taken from me, I made the choice.
It means that some of my heart's desires may go unfulfilled...
But many more are satisfied...
It is a good choice.

EPILOGUE
SHE CALLS HERSELF "AUDREY MARGUERITE" NOW. AND IN THREE DAYS, SHE'LL MARRY ONE OF BRAZIL'S WEALTHIEST MEN.
AND TWO WEEKS FROM THEN, HE'LL BE KILLED IN A CAR BOMB EXPLOSION.
"DRUG LORDS DID THIS." SHE'S ALREADY PRACTICING HER LINE IN SPANISH.
ESTE CALOR...
EXCUSE ME. YOU ARE BLOCKING MY SUN.
A MAN GAVE ME THIS TO GIVE TO YOU.
CONFESS
...AND SHE KNOWS SHE HAS NO CHOICE...

TS·94

MADNESS

TWO

Dear Diary...
~~My Dad~~...
~~Uncle Jim~~...
~~Jim~~...
He finally let me spend the whole day in the city...
...by myself!
...honestly... he thinks I'm a child!
DIARY
...It's madness...
...trying to raise one child in this city...
...let alone two.
...agreeing to adopt Babs...
What could I have been thinking?
...Then I see her smile...
...and I remember why.
HI.
IS THERE ANYTHING LEFT IN THE STORES?
VERY FUNNY.
LET'S GO HOME.
OH, AND DON'T WORRY...
I WON'T TELL MOM--
--YOU WERE SMOKING.

Tonight is Halloween.
Children should be allowed to dress up as spooks and fairies and collect candy...
...without having to worry about being poisoned...molested... or worse...

In the past weeks, reports of runaways disappearing near Gotham Central Park...
... led me to Jervis Tetch.
Delusional. Schizophrenic. Homicidal.
The Mad Hatter
is in Gotham City.
In this Style
TWINKLE, TWINKLE, LITTLE BAT!

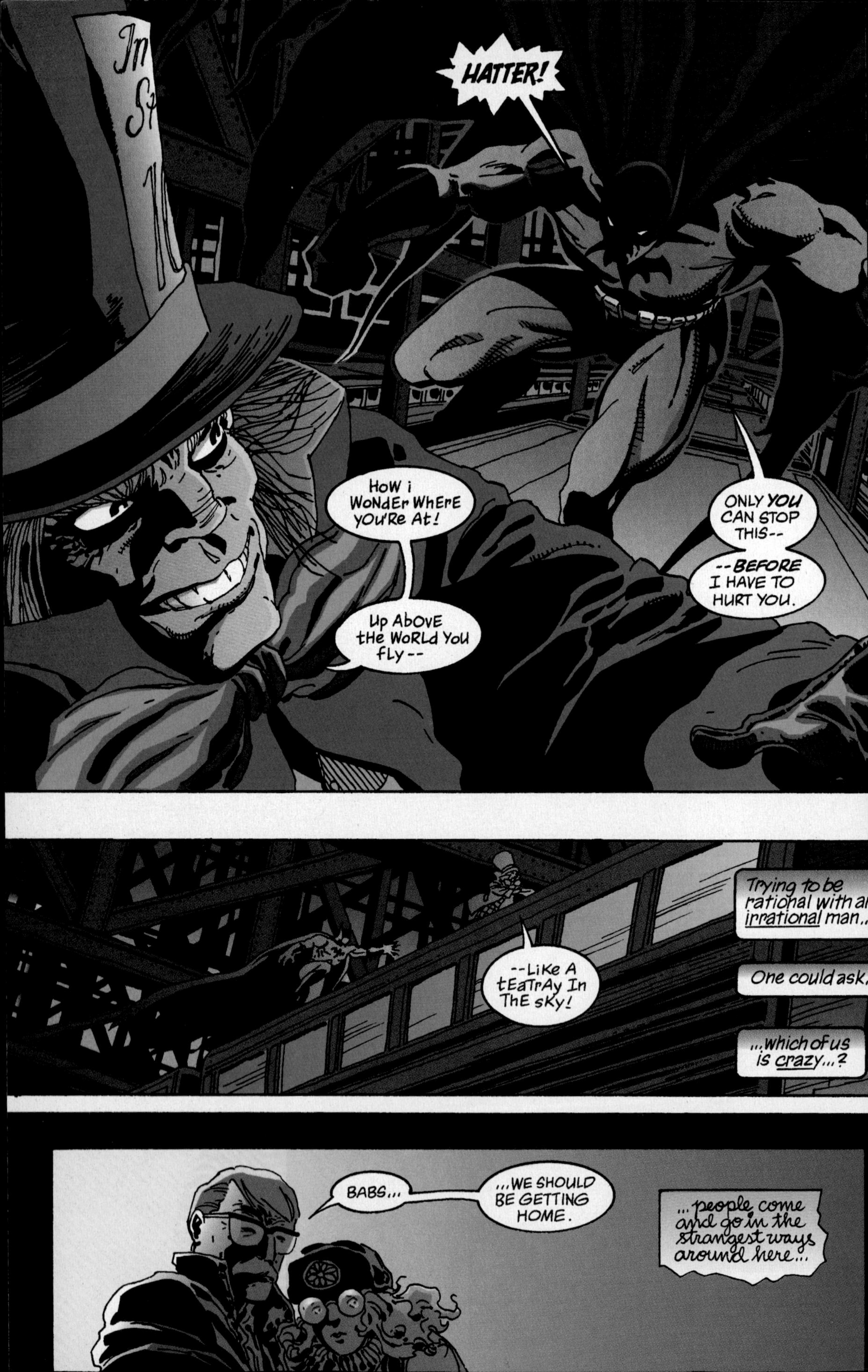

HATTER!

HOW i WONDEr WhErE YOU'RE At!

Up ABOVE tHe WORLd YOU fLY--

ONLY *YOU* CAN STOP THIS--

--*BEFORE* I HAVE TO HURT YOU.

Trying to be rational with a
irrational man..

--LiKE A tEaTrAy In ThE sKy!

One could ask,

...which of us is crazy...?

Joker. Scarecrow. Two-face.
Each has their own private madness that drives them.
Each has an unpredictable violent nature which makes them dangerous.
But, facing them does not disturb me...
... the way The Hatter does...
ROOMS
I·J·B

RILEY'S MAN
In taking his identity from "Alice in Wonderland"...
Jervis Tetch unknowingly perverts a happy childhood memory...
...of which I have so few...
...and reminds me of her...
...which I cannot afford to have happen.
MARIO'S
PRIV
AT THEATERS
EVE

GOTHAM PLAYING CARD Co
TAKE OFF YOUR HAT!
I KEEP THEM TO SELL.
I HAVE NONE OF MY OWN.
I'M A HATTER!

OFF.
OFF.
OFF.

THE QUEEN.

...WITH HIS HEAD!

TETCH.
I'M WILLING TO GIVE YOU A CHANCE.

tHe tImE hAs COmE...

YES...
...TO TALK... OF MANY THINGS...

oF sHOEs!

NO. THE CHILDREN.
THE MISSING CHILDREN.

--aNd ShIpS--

COOPERATE.

--aNd SeALiNg WaX!

i'M LaTe.

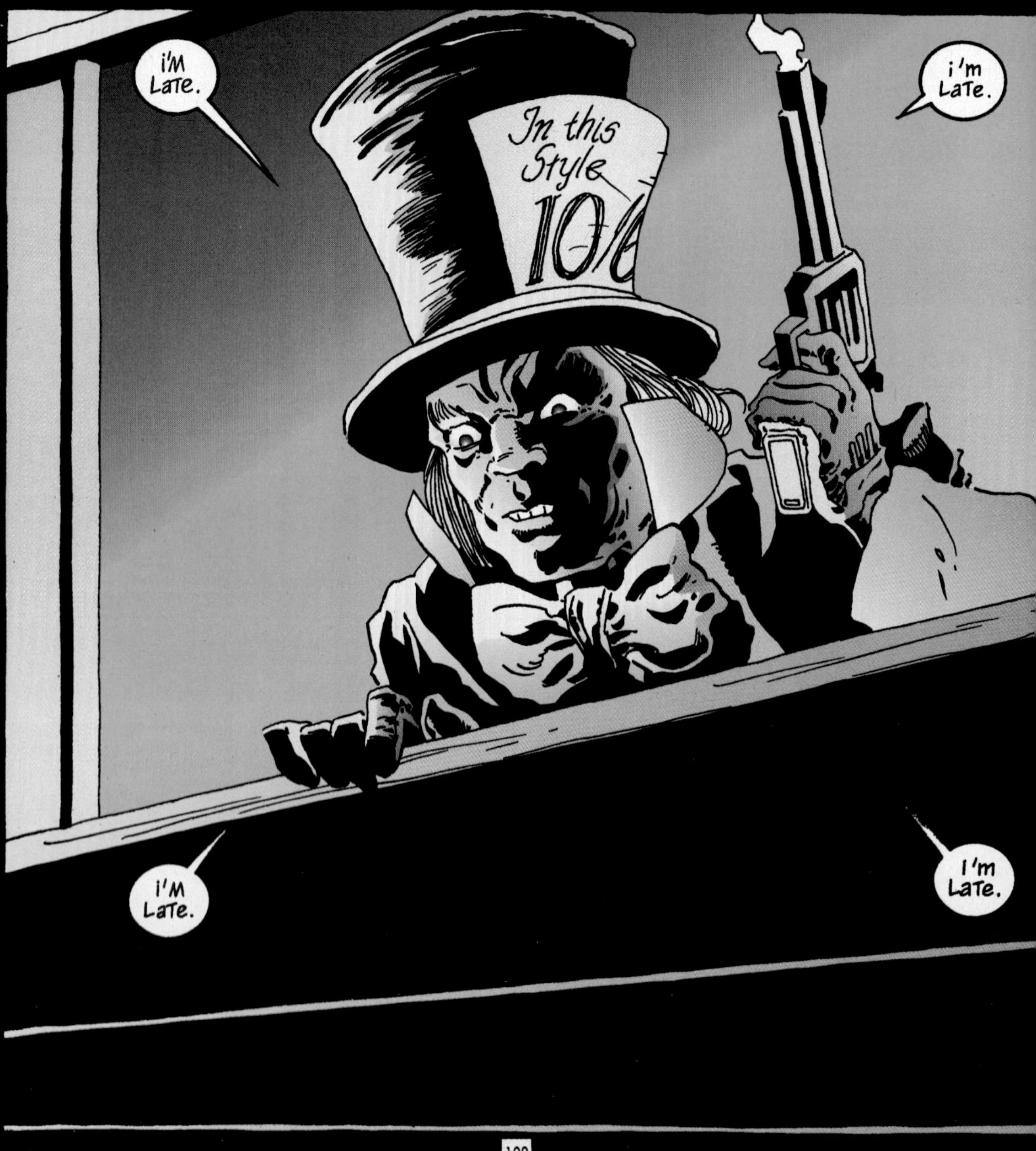

In this Style 10/6

i'm LaTe.

i'M LaTe.

I'm LaTe.

--WE'VE BEEN OVER THIS ALREADY AND--
BARBARA, I CAN'T HEAR MYSELF THINK!

THE BABY'S JUST A BIT FUSSY, JIM--
WAAA-WAAA!

MOM, WILL YOU SPEAK TO HIM?
OH NO, THIS IS BETWEEN YOU TWO.

HE'S NOT A BABY ANYMORE.
IF YOU WOULD TAKE HIM OFF BOTTLES--

SHH-SHH-SHHHHH...
WAAAA-WAAAA!
THERE YOU GO AGAIN!

PUSHING YOUR SON TO GROW UP--
--BUT WHEN IT COMES TO ME--

YOUNG LADY, I'VE GIVEN YOU A GREAT DEAL OF FREEDOM--

--FAR MORE THAN I HAD AT YOUR AGE!
THEN LET ME GO OUT TONIGHT! IT'S HALLOWEEN!

DON'T YOU TRUST ME?

THIS ISN'T ABOUT TRUST!

GOTHAM CITY ISN'T SOME SMALL TOWN IN OHIO--
--YOU'VE TOLD ME A MILLION TIMES!
--DON'T TAKE THAT TONE WITH ME!

OH, BUT IT'S OKAY FOR YOU TO SCREAM YOUR BRAINS OUT AT ME!

Sometimes, I envy The Batman...

I can't imagine that behind that mask, he hides a wife and children in Gotham.

I don't think he'd answer my signal in the night...

...if he had someone waiting for him at home.

THAT WENT WELL...

SLAM!

GOD BLESS OUR HOME

No... he gets to put on a <u>cape</u>--

--and leave <u>that</u> responsibility to the rest of us...

...bleeding... ...gunshot... ...Had... ...Matter... ...water... ...dripping ...stay conscious ...can't... remember her... rainy days... ...Mat Hadder... ...the gentle touch... ...Hats... ...her voice... ...rain-ing... ...Mad ... ...

WHAT GOOD'S A BOOK WITHOUT ANY PICTURES?
BRUCE, YOU SOUND LIKE ALICE!
WHO'S ALICE?
SHE'S THE ONE WHO HAS THE ADVENTURE.
WILL I LIKE IT?
IT'S JUST THE THING FOR A RAINY DAY...
"ALICE WAS BEGINNING TO GET TIRED OF SITTING BY HER SISTER ON THE BANK...
"...SUDDENLY A WHITE RABBIT WITH PINK EYES RAN BY...
"...ALICE FOUND HERSELF FALLING DOWN WHAT SEEMED TO BE A DEEP WELL...
"...CURIOUSER AND CURIOUSER, SHE CRIED...
"...THE CATERPILLAR AND ALICE LOOKED AT EACH OTHER FOR A LONG MOMENT...
"THERE WAS A TABLE SET UNDER A TREE AND THE MARCH HARE AND THE HATTER..."
BRUCE... WE'VE GOT TO STOP NOW--
PLEASE, JUST A LITTLE MORE...!
I'M GLAD YOU'RE ENJOYING IT, BUT--
YOU TWO AREN'T READY YET?
...FATHER...
COME ON NOW, WE DON'T WANT TO BE LATE...

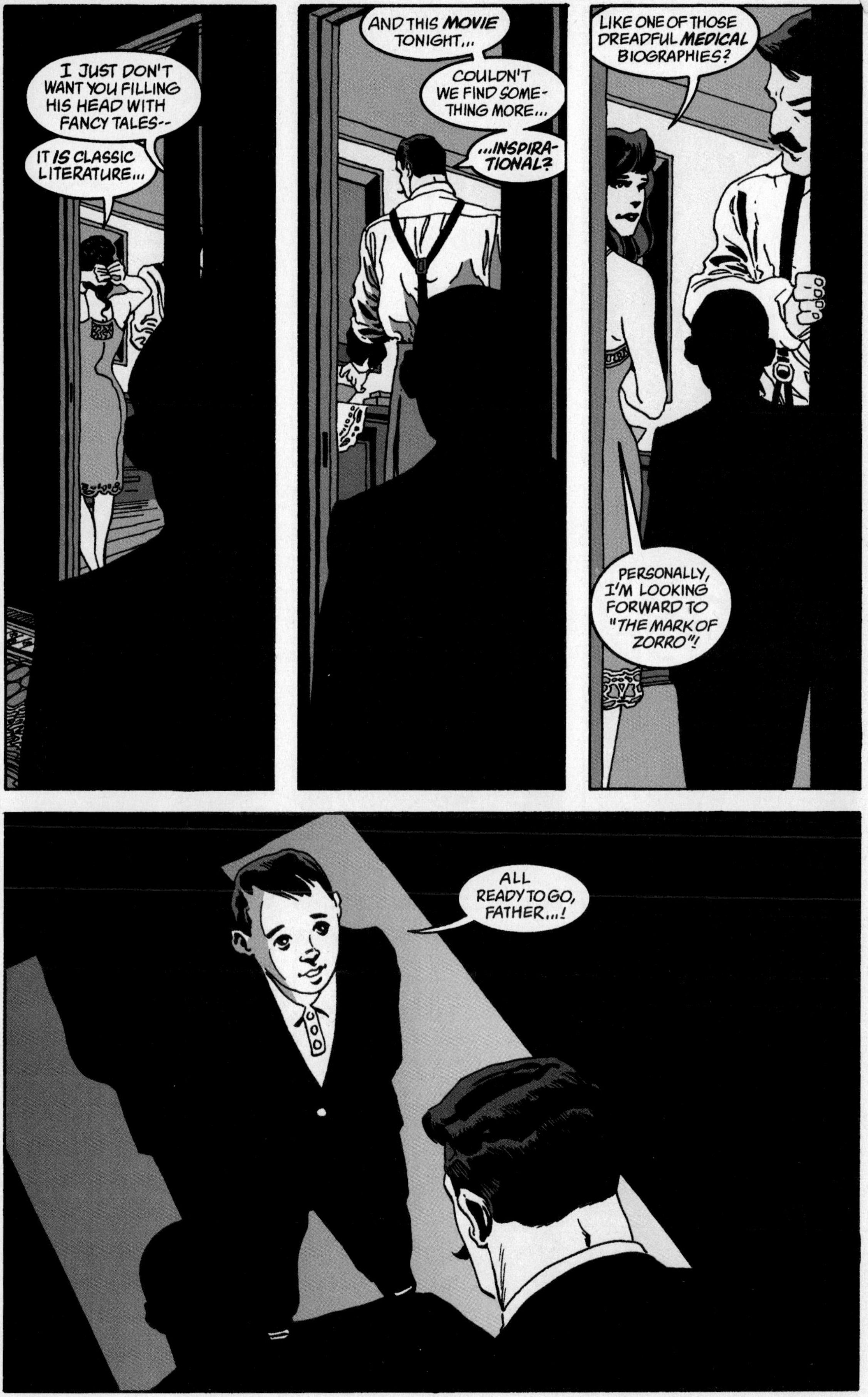

ALL READY TO GO, FATHER...!

WILL YOU WEAR THESE TONIGHT?

HONEY, WE'RE ONLY GOING TO THE MOVIES.
PEARLS ARE FOR A SPECIAL NIGHT.

COULDN'T WE MAKE IT SPECIAL?

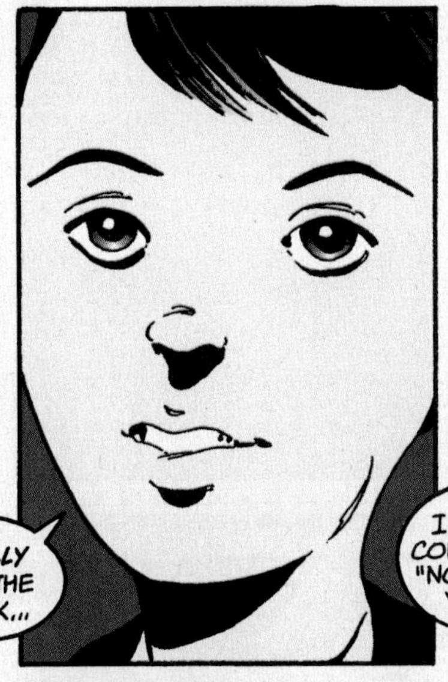
I REALLY LIKED THE BOOK...

I NEVER COULD SAY "NO" TO YOU...

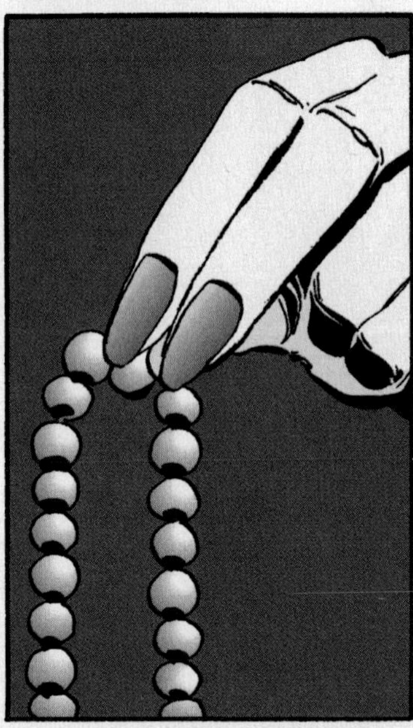

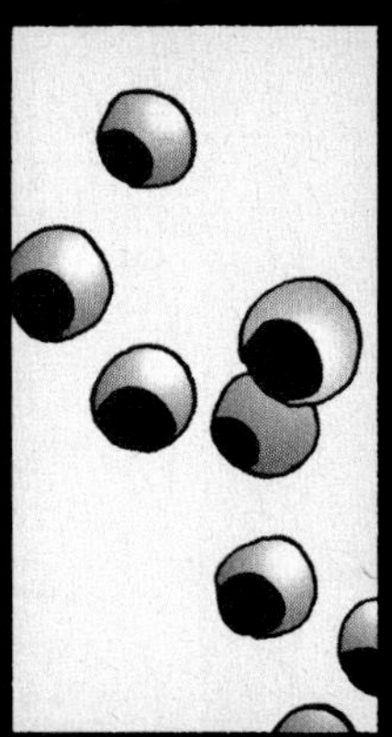
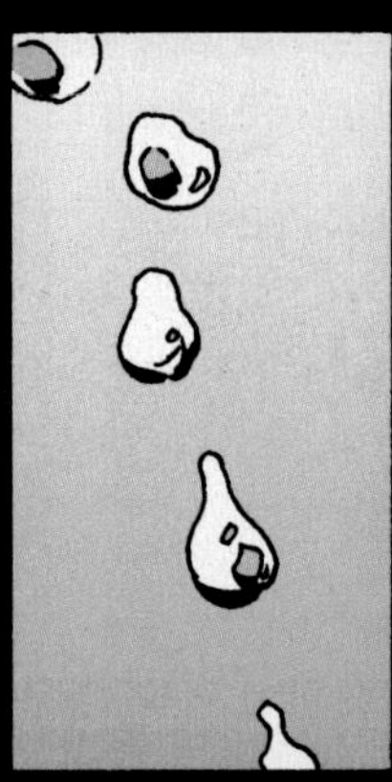

MOTHER!

MOTHER...
I never saw her again...

ALL RIGHT. YOU'VE PUNISHED ME ENOUGH.
LET'S AT LEAST DISCUSS IT--
BABS...?
DIARY
...He is my Dad and... He isn't my Dad...
I try my best... He doesn't try at all!
Why doesn't he understand...? He'll never understand...
Maybe I just don't belong here...
JIM...?
SHE'S...GONE, BARBARA.
I'VE SCARED OUR LITTLE GIRL AWAY...
THEN, YOU'D BETTER GET OFF YOUR DUFF--
--AND GET HALF THE CITY OUT LOOKING FOR HER!

TERRIFIC.
HERE I AM. ON MY OWN.
NO PLACE TO GO.
PROBABLY SCARING THE WITS OUT OF MOM AND--
TRICK OR TREAT!
SMELL MY FEET!
GIVE US SOMETHING GOOD TO EAT!
LATER!

I *HATE* IT WHEN HE'S RIGHT...
THIS IS ABOUT AS MUCH LIKE *OHIO* AS--
IF YOU DON'T--
--WE DON'T CARE!
--WE'LL PULL DOWN YOUR UNDER-WEA--
HELP!

BLAM

WHO THE--?

BLAM

LET'S GET OUTTA HERE!

BLAM

DON'T--
--HURT ME.

BLAM

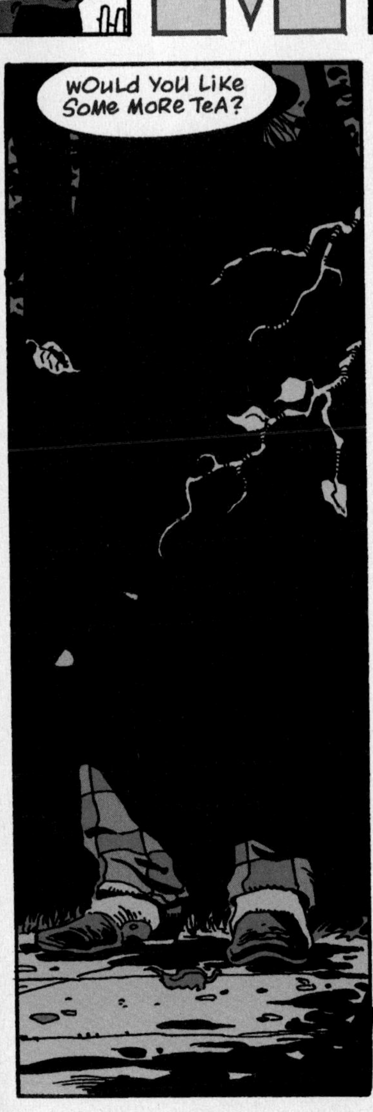
WOULD YOU LIKE SOME MORE TEA?

SHE CAN'T HAVE MORE TEA WHEN SHE HASN'T HAD ANY.

ACTUALLY, SHE CAN'T HAVE ANY LESS.

YOU COULD ALWAYS HAVE *MORE*.
COULDN'T YOU, ALICE?

Seems I've fallen down a hole...
With the amount of blood I've lost... And a useless right arm...
I can't go back the way I came.

SCREE
SCREE

"O MOUSE...
"...DO YOU KNOW THE WAY OUT OF THIS POOL?"
I'm coming for you, Tetch.

...head spinning... where...
...am I?
NO EXIT
LET ME HELP YOU...!
YOU?!
...Mother..?

CRIME ALLEY
PARK ROW
...madness...

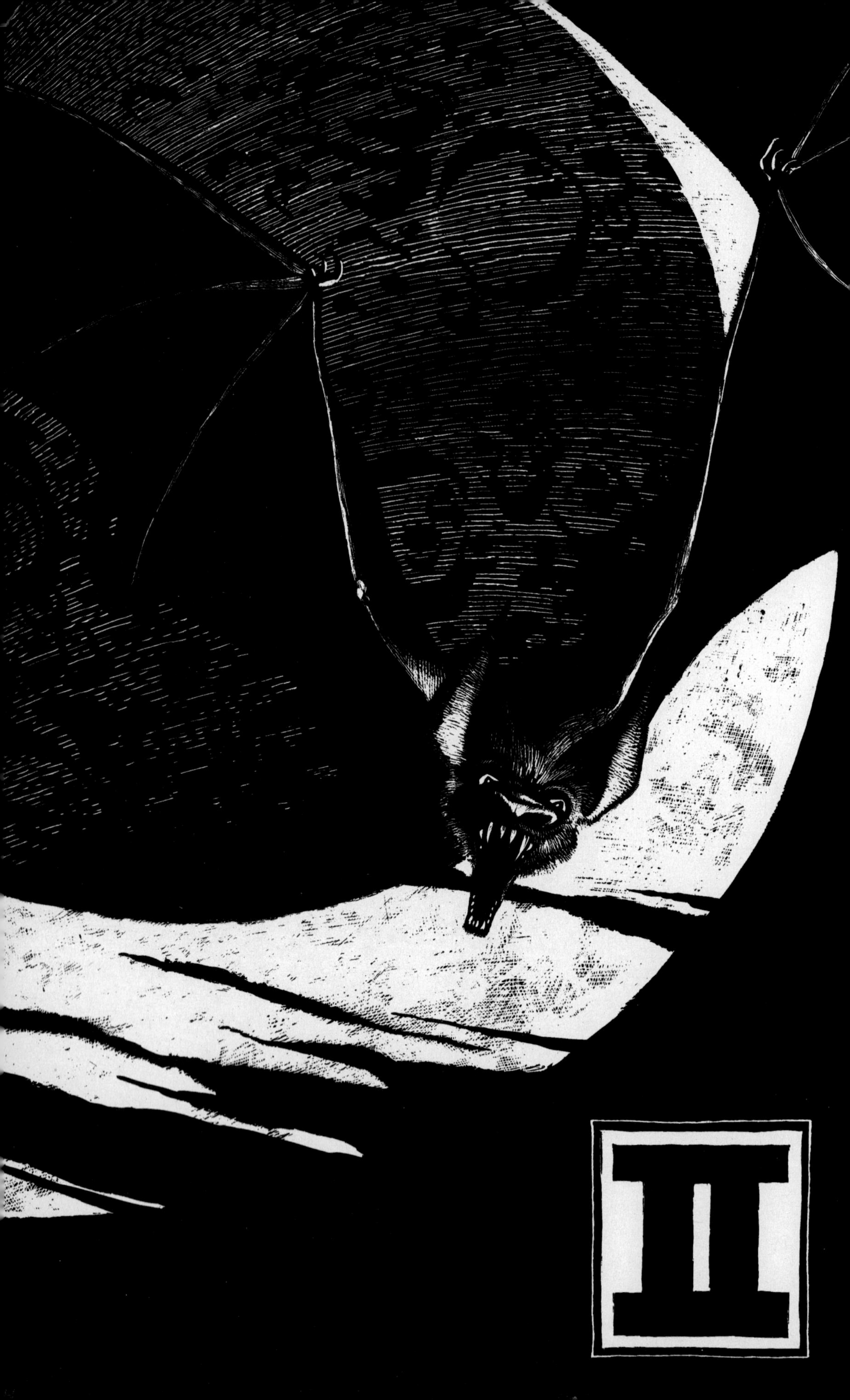
II

Dear Diary... I'm scared.
I see the light in the sky and I hope and pray that help is coming and...
ORANGE SPICE? EARL GREY? CONSTANT COMMENT?
...I have to try and think like he would. Like a cop.

He'd probably go along with whatever this crazy man wanted until...
CHINA ROSE? CHAMOMILE? JASMINE?
...his friend showed up.

His Dark Knight.
FORMOSA! OOLONG! RED ZINGER!
But... I'm scared...

It's quite Rude NOT to hAVE aNy TeA!
I DON'T MEAN TO BE RUDE.
REALLY.
I JUST... DON'T LIKE TEA.
HAVE SOME TEA KID.
HE DON'T LIKE WHEN W DON'T DRINK THE TEA.

In this style 10/6
OH, NO.
SHE DOESN'T LIKE TEA!

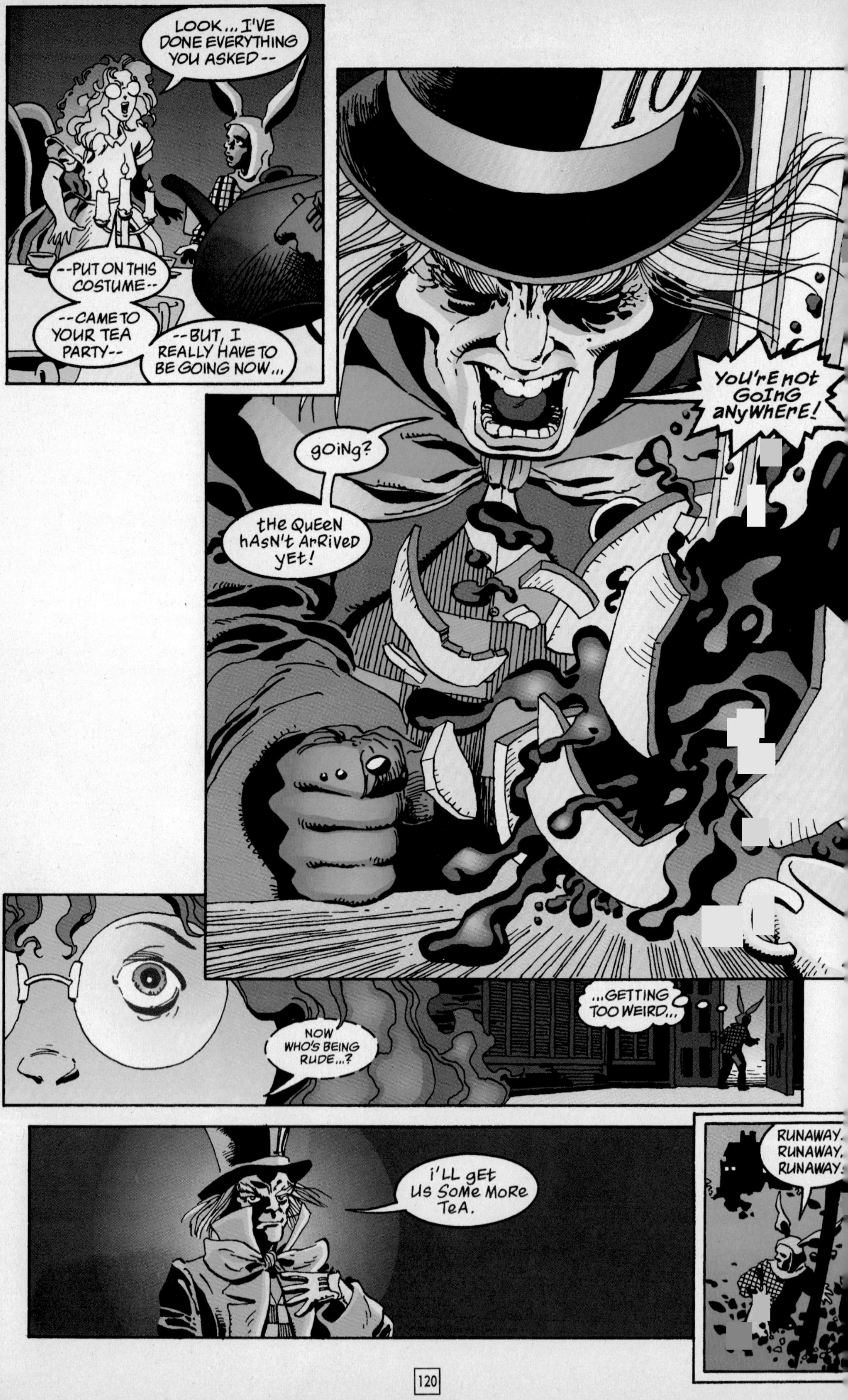

LOOK... I'VE DONE EVERYTHING YOU ASKED--
--PUT ON THIS COSTUME--
--CAME TO YOUR TEA PARTY--
--BUT, I REALLY HAVE TO BE GOING NOW...
YOU'RE NOT GOING ANYWHERE!
GOING?
THE QUEEN HASN'T ARRIVED YET!
NOW WHO'S BEING RUDE...?
...GETTING TOO WEIRD...

I keep going over and over it in my head--
--what I'll say to Babs when I find her.
How I'll make it right for her.
So we'll never have to go through this nightmare again...

No word.
No word from Batman.
No word on Babs.

This city never seemed quite as enormous--
--before I lost my child in it.

God, please, give me the chance to make it right.

YOU'VE LOST A LOT OF BLOOD. I HAVE TO TAKE THIS OFF TO--
DON'T...
YOU'RE HURTING ME!
...MOTHER?
...CAN'T BE...
...CAN'T BE...
I'D LIKE TO HELP YOU... IF YOU'LL LET ME.

...Leslie...!

I'M DR. THOMPKINS.
I'D LIKE TO HELP YOU... IF YOU'LL LET ME.

BRUCE?

ALFRED THOUGHT I MIGHT FIND YOU IN HERE.
I'VE BROUGHT YOU SOMETHING--
--FOUND IT DOWNSTAIRS IN THE LIBRARY.

Alice's Adventures in Wonderland
Lewis Carroll
IT'S JUST THE THING FOR A RAINY DAY--

I HATE THAT BOOK!

I DON'T WANT YOUR HELP!

I DON'T WANT ANYBODY TO--

--HELP ME...

I THINK HE'S FINALLY ASLEEP.
HONESTLY, MR. PENNYWORTH, I THOUGHT HE WOULD ENJOY THE BOOK.

APPARENTLY WE WERE BOTH MISTAKEN.
I HOPE SOMEDAY THAT BRUCE WILL COME BACK TO THE THINGS--
--THAT REMIND HIM OF HIS PARENTS.

BUT THE BOY IS SO DETERMINED--
--LEFT TO HIMSELF, HE'D SHUT EVERYTHING OUT OF HIS LIFE.

THEN, WE NEED TO BE EQUALLY DETERMINED IN OUR LOVE FOR HIM...

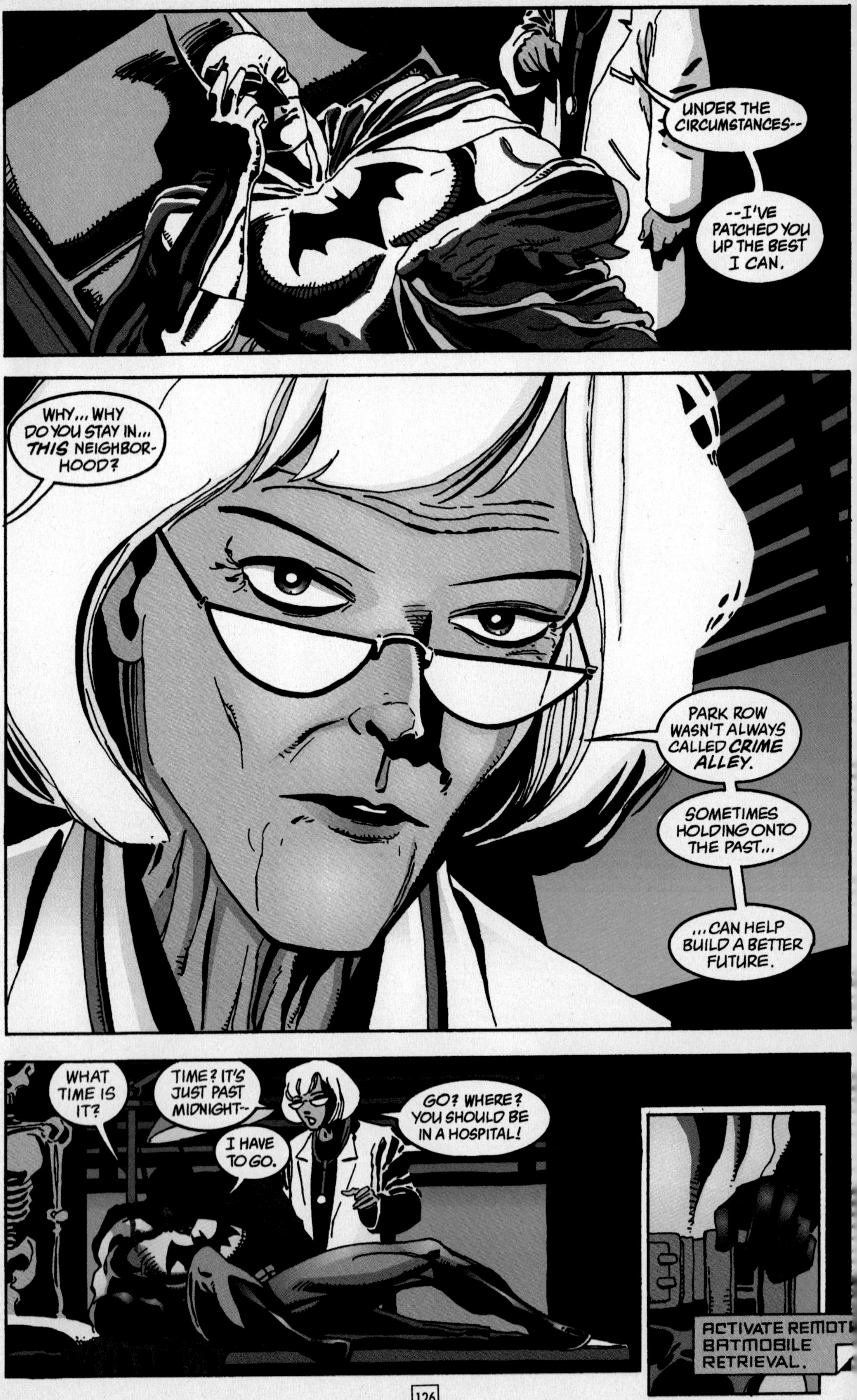

WHY... WHY DO YOU STAY IN... *THIS* NEIGHBOR-HOOD?

PARK ROW WASN'T ALWAYS CALLED *CRIME ALLEY.*

SOMETIMES HOLDING ONTO THE PAST...

...CAN HELP BUILD A BETTER FUTURE.

DOCTOR THOMPKINS...
THANK YOU.
FOR TONIGHT...
...AND OR MORE HAN YOU CAN KNOW.

PARK ROW CLINIC
PARK ROW CLINIC
In the pain that was my childhood.
And the horror that changed my life.
COMMENCE SCANNING ALL POLICE BANDS.
211 IN PROGRESS. CITY LIQUOR.

Had it not been for the death of my parents--
--I would never come to know...
DOMESTIC DISPUTE IN GOTHAM TOWERS.

...a remarkable woman.
ALL UNITS IN VICINITY. SUSPECT KNOWN AS JERVIS TETCH LOCATED--

Hill House. One of the first cases I ever worked on here.
Two brothers. Sam and Nat Hill. Rich. Society set. Bored. Decided to kidnap a six-year-old boy. For kicks.
Ransom was paid. The perfect crime.
But, the Hills were afraid the boy would identify them.
The brothers murdered the child in that house and...
...I saw to it the bastards went to the electric chair.
The house fell into disrepair. No one would live here after that...

...no one but a madman.
ON MY COMMAND--
The March Hare gave it all up.
The layout of the house.
The number of armed guards.
The room the Hatter is in...

My men are ready to go...
...then I think of Babs' smile...
...what if something goes wrong? What if--
tap
tap

TELL YOUR MEN TO *HOLD* THEIR POSITIONS.
YOU!

TETCH HAS MAYBE A DOZEN OR SO CHILDREN, RUNAWAYS, INSIDE.
SOME SORT OF... INSANE TEA PARTY.

KEEPS THEM--SEDATED--
--MAKING THEM DRINK DRUGGED TEA.

THE ONE DRESSED AS "ALICE"--
--MATCHES THE DESCRIPTION OF MY *DAUGHTER*...

I know what has to be done...

TOK
BDFFF
Don't know how long Gordon will wait.
With his child in danger, he'll react emotionally.
I fool myself into thinking I'm stronger than that...
WE'RE ALL MAD HERE.
I'M MAD.
YOU'RE MAD.
SHHHH.
HOW DO YOU KNOW I'M MAD?
YOU MUST BE--
--OR YOU WOULDN'T HAVE COME HERE.

tHe QUEEN OF hEArts
In this Style 10/6
sHe MaDe some TArTS
In this Style 10/6
aLL ON a SUMMEr's dAy,
In this Style 10/6
tHe KNAVE OF hEArtS
hE sTOLe THOSE tArts
aND TOOK THEM QUITE AWAY!

i'M LaTe.
i'm LaTe.
i'M LaTe.
i'm LaTe.
Every scenario I think of...
...winds up with Gordon's daughter hurt or--

BABS!
IS SHE ALL RIGHT?
SHE WILL BE...
GET THE HATTER.
YOU THERE! OUT OF THE WAY!

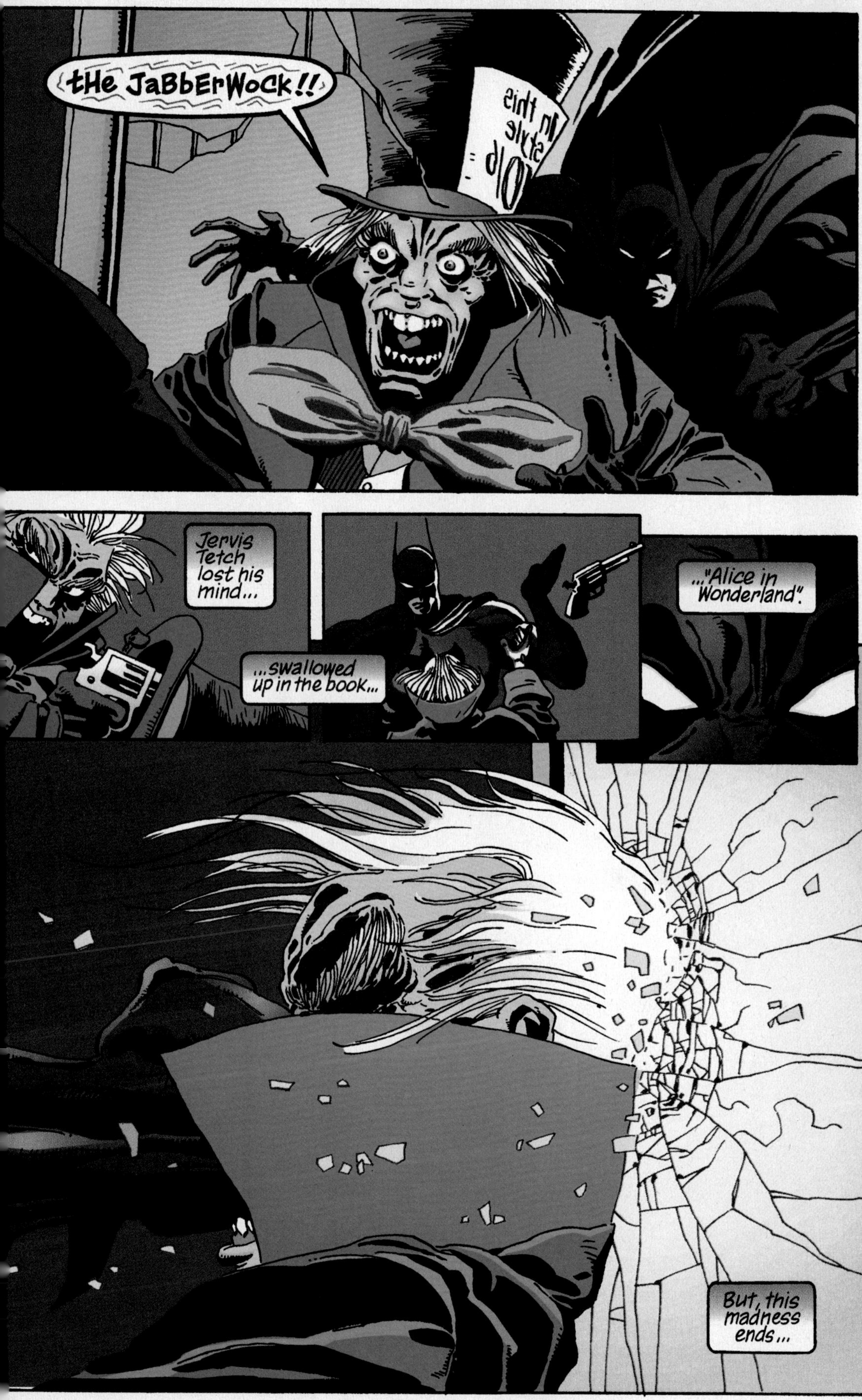

Jervis Tetch lost his mind...

...swallowed up in the book...

..."Alice in Wonderland".

But, this madness ends...

...through the looking glass.

RUNAWAYS, MOSTLY. TETCH PROMISED THEM A HOME...OF SORTS...
I KNOW A WOMAN... A DOCTOR... WHO CAN HELP THEM...
...IF THEY'LL LET HER...

I... WANTED TO SAY...I'M SORRY...

...ALL THE TROUBLE I CAUSED AND--

...people come and go in the strangest ways around here...

HE DOES IT TO ME ALL THE TIME.

DADDY.
I'D... LIKE TO COME HOME.

BABS. I...
YES. LET'S GO HOME.

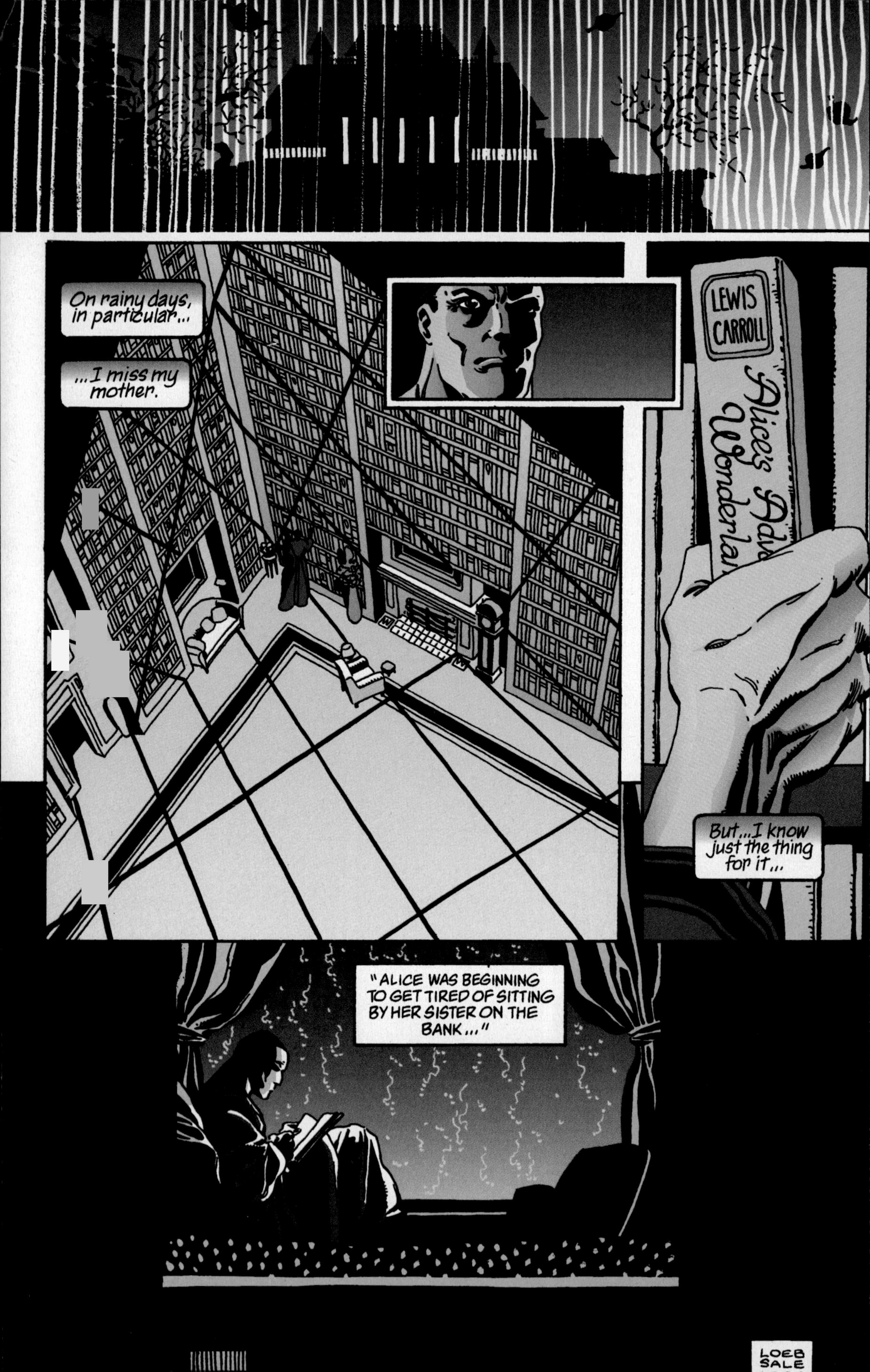

On rainy days, in particular...

...I miss my mother.

LEWIS CARROLL

Alice's Adv... Wonderla...

But...I know just the thing for it...

"ALICE WAS BEGINNING TO GET TIRED OF SITTING BY HER SISTER ON THE BANK..."

LOEB SALE 1994

TIM
SALE
1995

GHOSTS

THREE

'Twas the night before Halloween...
BRUCE?
LUCIUS?
IT'S BEEN YEARS...
NO... HAS IT?
AND NOW, HERE WE ARE, BACK IN GOTHAM CITY OF ALL PLACES.
YOU KNOW WHAT I WISH?
HMMM?
I WISH YOU'D TAKEN ME UP ON THAT OFFER.
THE THINGS WE COULD HAVE ACCOM-PLISHED.
I...OFTEN FIND MYSELF WITH MISSED OPPORTUNITIES, LUCIUS.
DON'T TAKE IT PERSONALLY.

While attending another in the endless array of charitable functions I endure...

...the unexpected happens with a terrible swiftness.

Despite his...unnatural appearance, Halloween has not begun a night early.
Disfigured since childhood, Oswald Chesterfield Cobblepot now bears the horrific resemblance of his chosen namesake:
The Penguin
HOW... DISAPPOINTING.
DESPITE THE MONETARY WHEREWITHAL TO INDULGE ONE'S PALATE --
-- YOUR EPICUREAN TASTES RUN TO THE MUNDANE.
WHILE I, ON THE OTHER HAND, INTEND TO FILL MY GULLET--

--UNTIL I HAVE FETED MY RAVENOUS APPETITE!
BLAM BLAM BLAM!
KCHOW KCHOW KCHOW KCHO
EVERYONE! DOWN!
A HERO.
ONE IN EVERY CROWD.
146

I ASSUME NO FURTHER INSTRUCTIONS ARE NECESSARY.
BRUCE WAYNE WAS A *GOOD* MAN--
--WHO WASTED THE MOST PRECIOUS *COMMODITY* WE ALL SHARE.
TIME.
NOW THEN, YOUR WALLET. AND THAT *MEDALLION*.
MY... MEDALLION...
INTERESTING BAUBLE.

The grand entrance is intentional.
I want Penguin's attention focused only on me.
Hopefully, minimalizing the casualties to one--

--the Penguin himself.
AHH... THE BATMAN.
WHILE I HAVE AN AFFECTION FOR MOST FLYING CREATURES--
--THE WINGED RAT IS NOT AMONG THEM.
DROP THE GUN.
NOW.

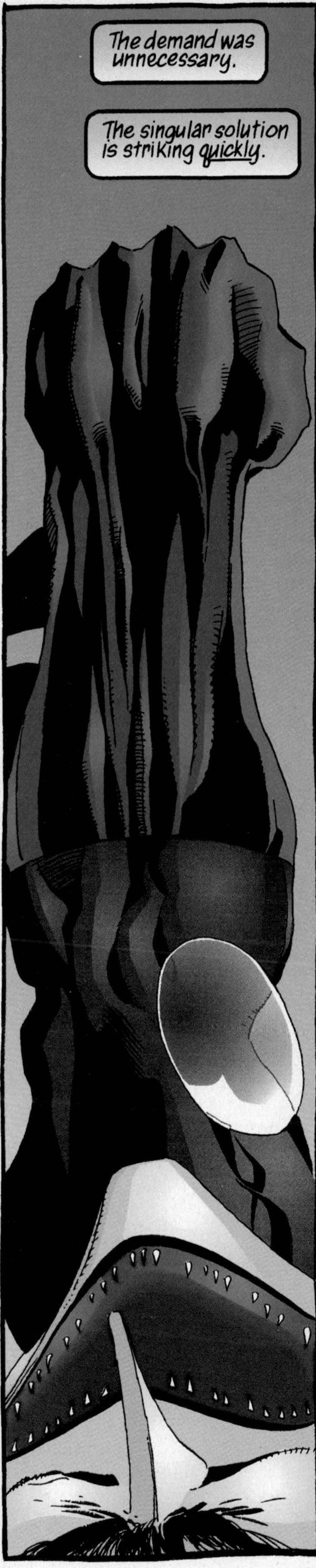
The demand was unnecessary.
The singular solution is striking quickly.

Relentlessly.

Some would say...

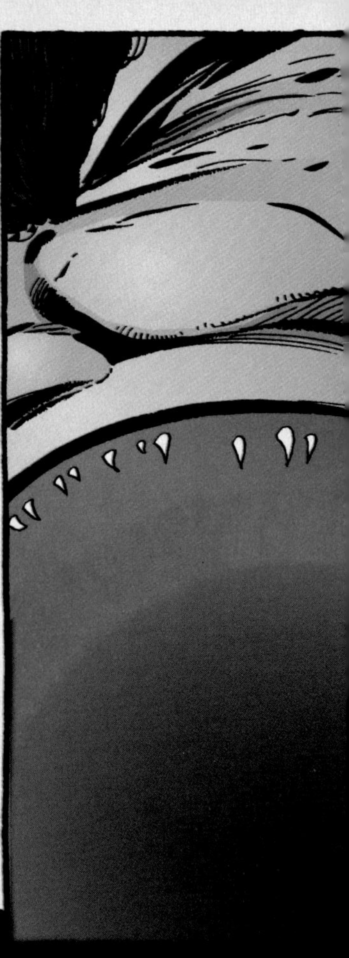

...savagely.

WHEN PARTAKING IN PURE FISTICUFFS--
--YOU HAVE ME AT A DISADVANTAGE.
AND RATHER THAN SUFFER TH
INDIGNITY OF ANOTHER DEFEA
-- I'LL TAKE MY LEAVE.
Innocent lives are at stake.
Almost any means justifies the ends.
GOOD-BYE, CRUEL WORLD!

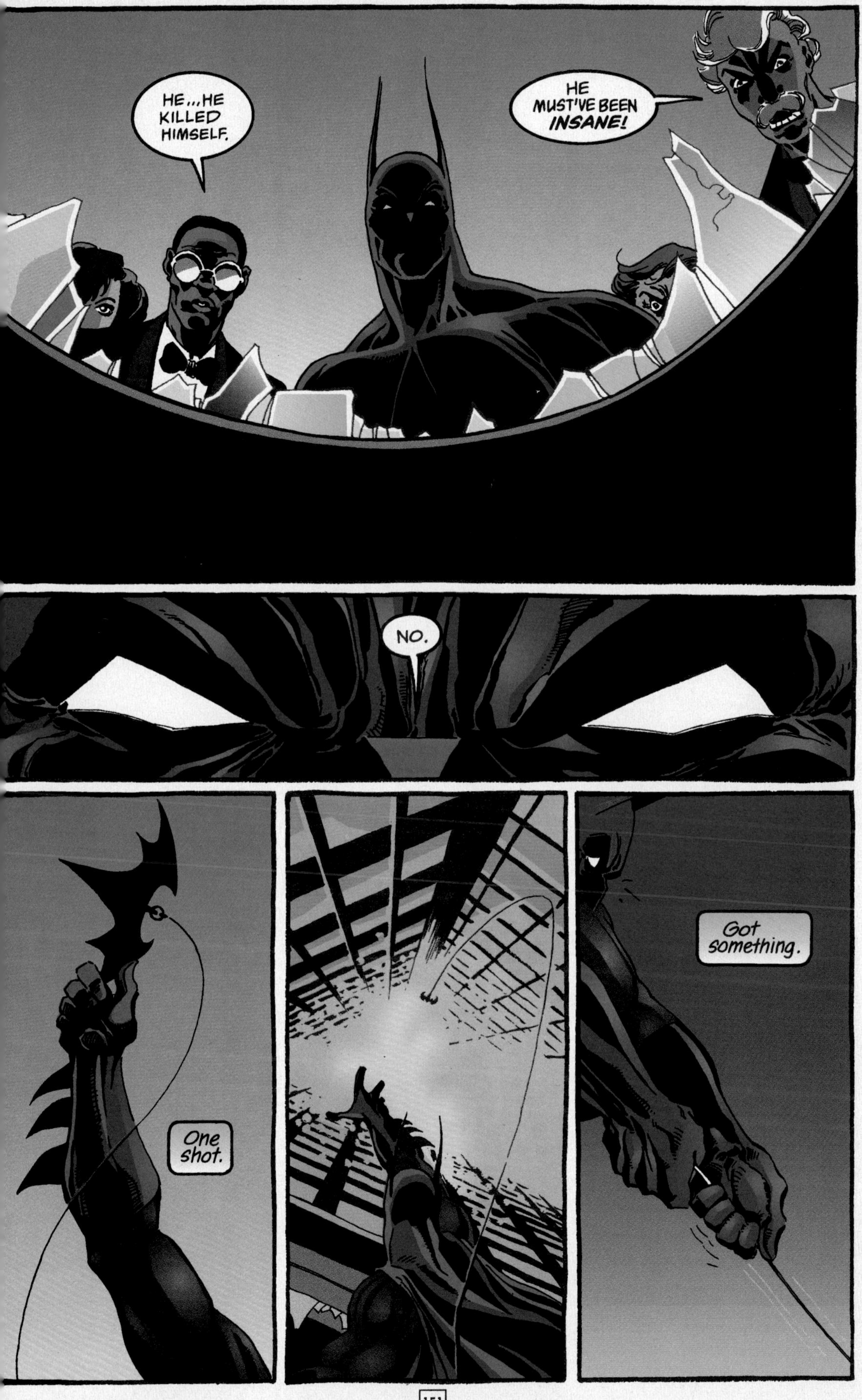

HE... HE KILLED HIMSELF.

HE MUST'VE BEEN *INSANE!*

A cobalt-driven single-stroke portable jet engine. Capable of accelerating to a three G-force.
Alfred informed me of the theft of a prototype from Gotham's Primatek Laboratories while updating the computer.

EH?
In other words...
...THIS PENGUIN FLIES!

YOU BLITHERING IDIOT!
WITH YOUR ADDED WEIGHT--
--YOU'LL KILL US BOTH!
OR.
LAND SAFELY.
IMMEDIATELY.
KCHING
I'D PREFER TO TAKE A CHANCE.
SCRATCHY SCRATCHY
AND CUT MY LOSSES.

The Penguin's uncooperative choice is not unexpected.

His overinflated ego defines his actions--

--limiting his ability to see the reasonable alternative--

--and leading to an extremely painful conclusion.

It is a luxury I cannot afford for myself.

As the protector of Gotham City's residents--
--justice must be blind.
Expedient.
And severe.
I have learned that my decisions cannot be encumbered by one's personal indulgences.
waugh...!

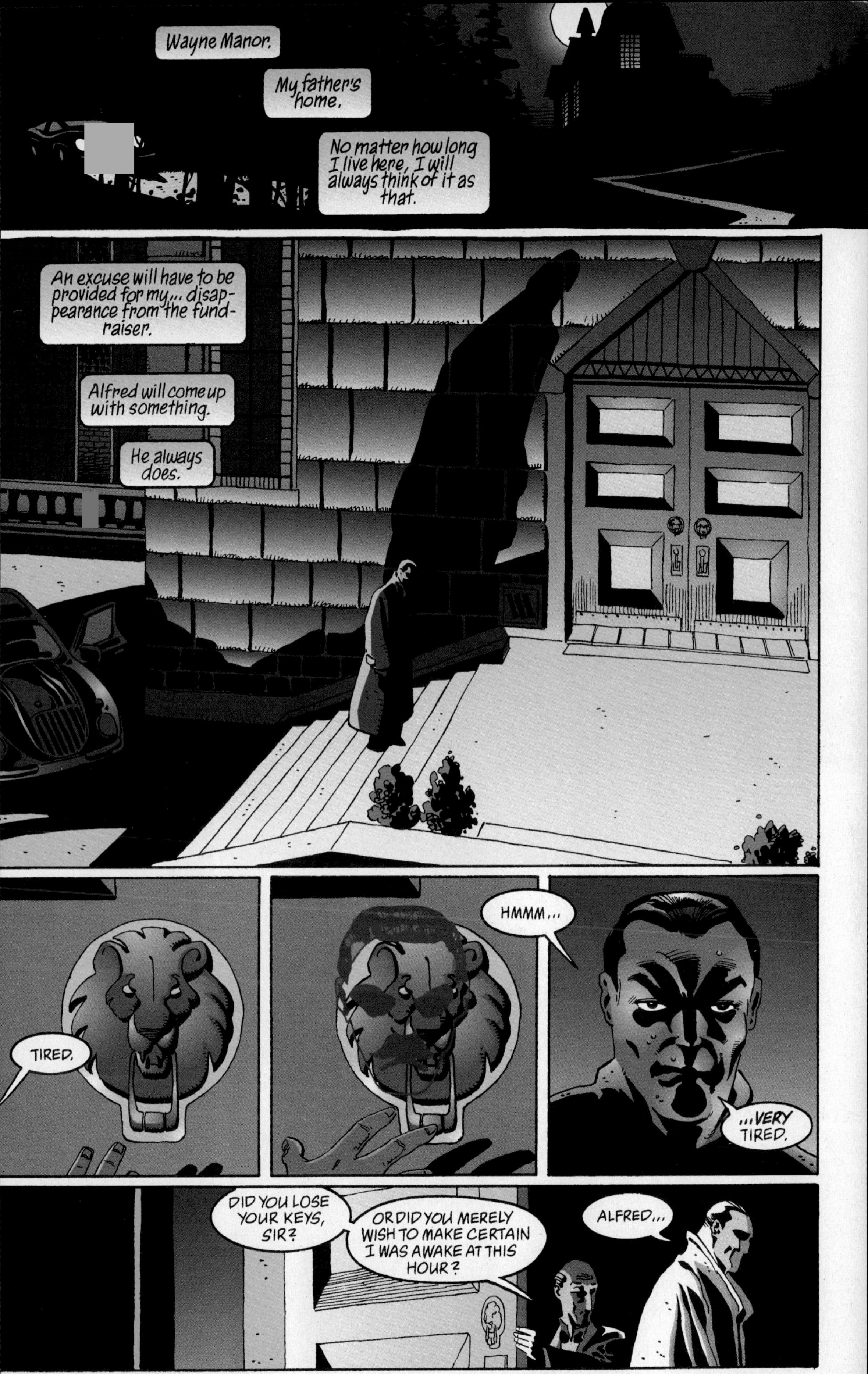

Wayne Manor.

My father's home.

No matter how long I live here, I will always think of it as that.

An excuse will have to be provided for my... disappearance from the fund-raiser.

Alfred will come up with something.

He always does.

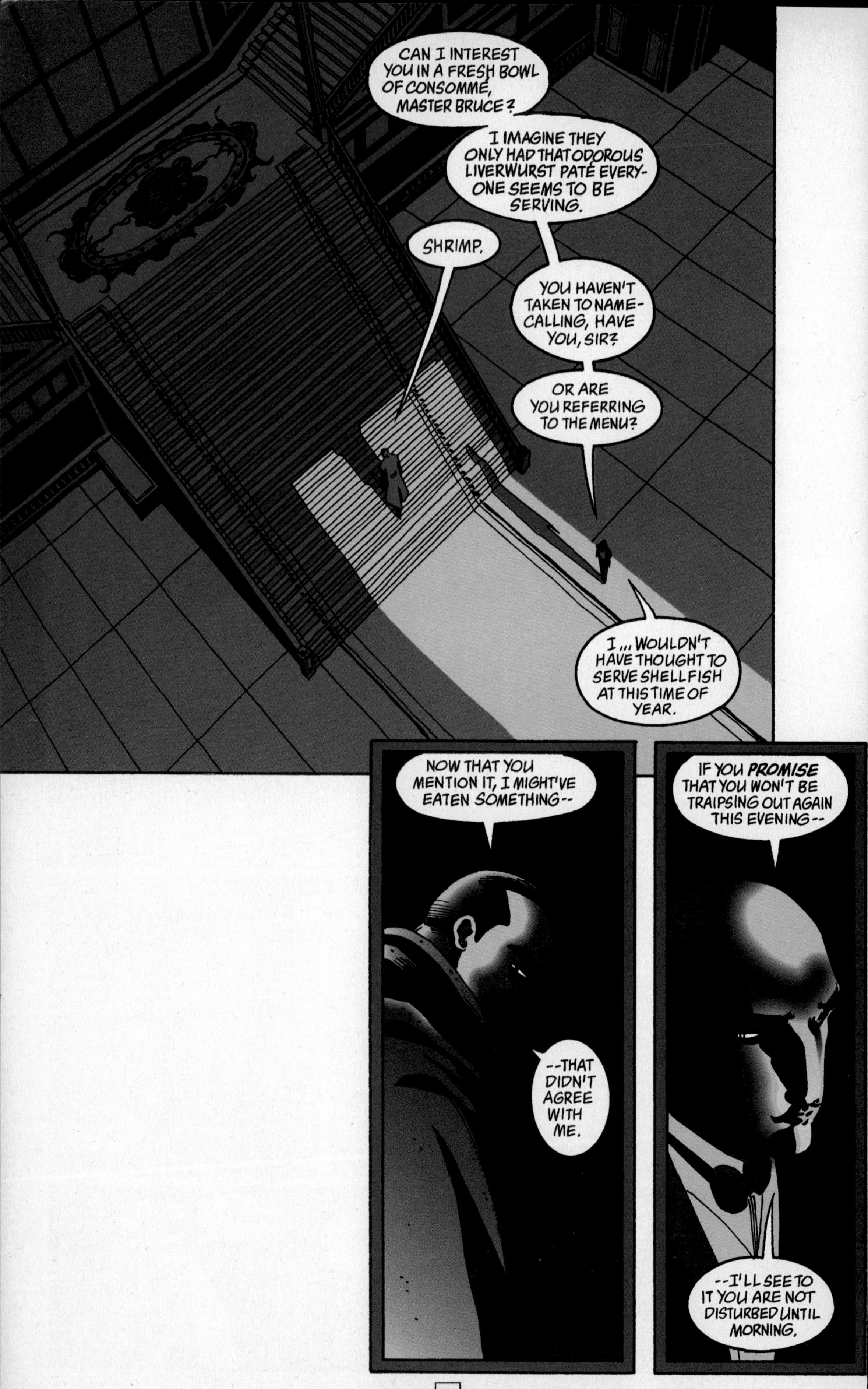

CAN I INTEREST YOU IN A FRESH BOWL OF CONSOMMÉ, MASTER BRUCE?
I IMAGINE THEY ONLY HAD THAT ODOROUS LIVERWURST PATÉ EVERY-ONE SEEMS TO BE SERVING.
SHRIMP.
YOU HAVEN'T TAKEN TO NAME-CALLING, HAVE YOU, SIR?
OR ARE YOU REFERRING TO THE MENU?
I... WOULDN'T HAVE THOUGHT TO SERVE SHELLFISH AT THIS TIME OF YEAR.

Can't sleep.
Feverish.
CLANK CHING CLANK
ALFRED...?
CLANK CHING CLANK
Perhaps that accounts for what I saw--
--or thought I saw--
--on the front door...
CLANK CHING CLANK
ALFRED, WHAT ARE YOU DOING OUT THERE?
CLANK CHING CLANK

Good evening.
Bruce.
M.D.
...FATHER...?

NO!
Do not waste the brief time we have by denying my existence before you.
Look, instead, long and hard at the weight I carry now.
These chains I wear I forged in life.
Link by link, yard by yard, I made this burden.
Obsessed with my medical practice, I lost sight of what was truly important.
THIS IS SOMEONE'S IDEA OF A HALLOWEEN JOKE--
--A PERVERSE PRANK!
YOU'RE WRONG! MY FATHER SAVED LIVES!
HE WAS A GREAT MAN!
Bruce...
I have risked much by coming to you and have done so out of love.
I pray I am not too late.
Your obsession with Batman--
--creates an even greater and more thunderous chain!

Tonight, beginning when the clock strikes "one"--
--you will be visited by the first of three spirits.
Hees their warnings, my son.
HEED THEIR WARNINGS!
HOW DARE YOU...!
HOW DARE YOU BREAK INTO MY HOME--
--DEFILE THE MEMORY OF MY FATHER!
I... I've been dreaming.
The fever.
There is no other explanation...

BONG
WHAT?
THE CLOCK ...?
WHAT'S HAPPENED HERE?!

HELLO, LOVER.
LONG TIME, NO SEE.
POISON IVY?!
Pamela Isley. Botanist turned madwoman.
Suddenly, it all begins to make sense...

I'M FLATTERED BY THE ACCUSATION, BUT I'M MERELY A PLAYER THIS EVENING--
--AND NOT THE PILOT.
THE REAL PAMELA ISLEY IS LOCKED SAFELY AWAY IN ARKHAM WHERE YOU PUT HER.
SOMEHOW YOU'VE POISONED ME.
INVADED MY HOME.
MY MIND.
WE SPIRITS MERELY CHOSE THESE FORMS BECAUSE OF WHO YOU ARE.
TO OTHERS WE MIGHT APPEAR AS SOMETHING OR SOMEONE ELSE...
DON'T... YOUR TOUCH... POISON...
RELAX.
DON'T FIGHT ME.
AND LET THE SPIRITS--
--AS THEY SAY--
--MOVE YOU...

RECOGNIZE THIS PLACE?
OF COURSE. WE'RE DOWNSTAIRS.
SUPPOSEDLY.
...BUT...
NO!
THIS IS... WAS... YEARS AGO...
MOTHER!
I'M READY TO GO!
That's... me!
OH, YOUR COSTUME LOOKS GREAT!
THANKS. I MADE IT MYSELF.
ALFRED SORTA HELPED.
IS DAD HOME YET?
BRUCE...
YOUR FATHER CALLED AND--
--DON'T TELL ME.
HE'S GOTTA WORK LATE...!

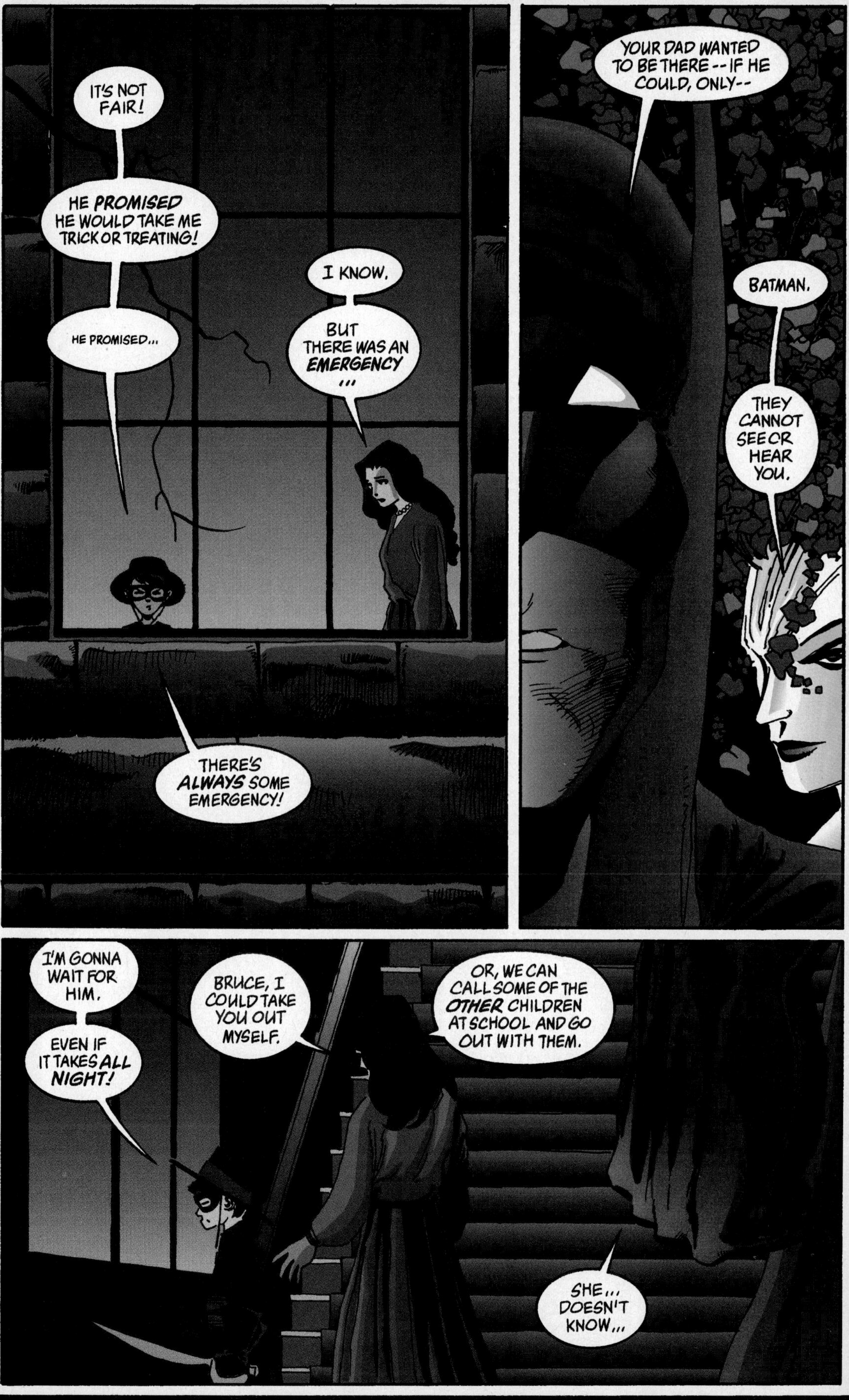

IT'S NOT FAIR!
HE *PROMISED* HE WOULD TAKE ME TRICK OR TREATING!
HE PROMISED...
I KNOW.
BUT THERE WAS AN *EMERGENCY* ...
THERE'S *ALWAYS* SOME EMERGENCY!

THERE ARE NO OTHER KIDS TO CALL.
I HAVE NO FRIENDS AT SCHOOL.
BRUCE...
IVY.
THIS HAS GONE ON LONG ENOUGH.
WHATEVER **SPELL** YOU PUT ME UNDER--
--YOU'VE MADE YOUR POINT.
REALLY.
I'M AFRAID YOU'RE GOING TO FIND THIS EVENING WON'T WORK LIKE THAT.
WE HAVE... **MUCH** MORE AHEAD OF US...

"...IN THE PAST..."
Paris. Notre Dame.
I came here after my parents died...
IVY. WHY ARE WE HERE?
SHH... PATIENCE.
IS EVERYTHING YOU DO DONE IN A HURRY?
That's... Lucius Fox... only younger...
RIEN DE JEUX. LE PRIX SEULMENT.
TON ARGENT, AMERICAIN.
HAVE TO DO SOMETHING--
--TO STOP THEM!

YOU DO.
REMEMBER?
Again... that's me!
I'd... forgotten how...
...reckless I could be back then.

WHAT YOU LACKED IN POLISH, YOU CERTAINLY MADE UP FOR IN EFFECTIVENESS.
I WAS... LEARNING. WITHOUT WEAPONS OR A COSTUME.
FOOLISH, REALLY.
AS OPPOSED TO SAILING ACROSS GOTHAM CITY WITH THE PENGUIN?
HOW COULD YOU KNOW ABOUT THAT?
HOW COULD YOU KNOW ABOUT ANY OF THIS?!
YOUR THINGS.
TH-THANKS. YOU'RE AN AMERICAN, HUH?
STAY OUT OF THIS NEIGHBORHOOD AT NIGHT.
IT'S DANGEROUS.
WAIT!
LET ME AT LEAST BUY YOU DINNER...

BRUCE. WAYNE.
THE BRUCE WAYNE?
JUST... BUMMING AROUND PARIS?
HMMM? YES, I SUPPOSE.
YOU KNOW, I'VE BEEN THINKING.
OUR MEETING TONIGHT COULD TURN OUT TO BE... FORTUITOUS.
FOR BOTH OF US.
HOW DO YOU MEAN?
MY EXPERTISE IS IN FINANCE--
--AND WITH YOUR FAMILY FORTUNE, WE COULD REALLY DO SOMETHING EXTRAORDINARY.
NO. THAT MONEY--
LIKE ME--
--HAS ALREADY BEEN COMMITTED ELSEWHERE.
KIND OF... ABRUPT, WEREN'T YOU?
HE WAS ONLY OFFERING YOU AN OPPORTUNITY...
LUCIUS WOULDN'T HAVE UNDERSTOOD.
NO ONE COULD.
I MADE A PROMISE.
TO HONOR MY PARENTS.
SOMEDAY TO RID GOTHAM CITY OF THE CRIME THAT TOOK THEIR LIVES.

IS THAT HOW YOUR PARENTS WOULD HAVE WANTED YOU TO HONOR THEM?

YOU WOULDN'T UNDERSTAND.
NO ONE COULD.

SO YOU'VE SAID...
...SO YOU'VE SAID...

Awake...!

HOME.
IN MY BED.
ALL OF IT... SOME KIND OF NIGHTMARE...
...THE SHRIMP I ATE...

The porcelain bowl feels cold.
My head feels hot.
BONG
BONG
he-Heee-Ho-ha!
Laughter?

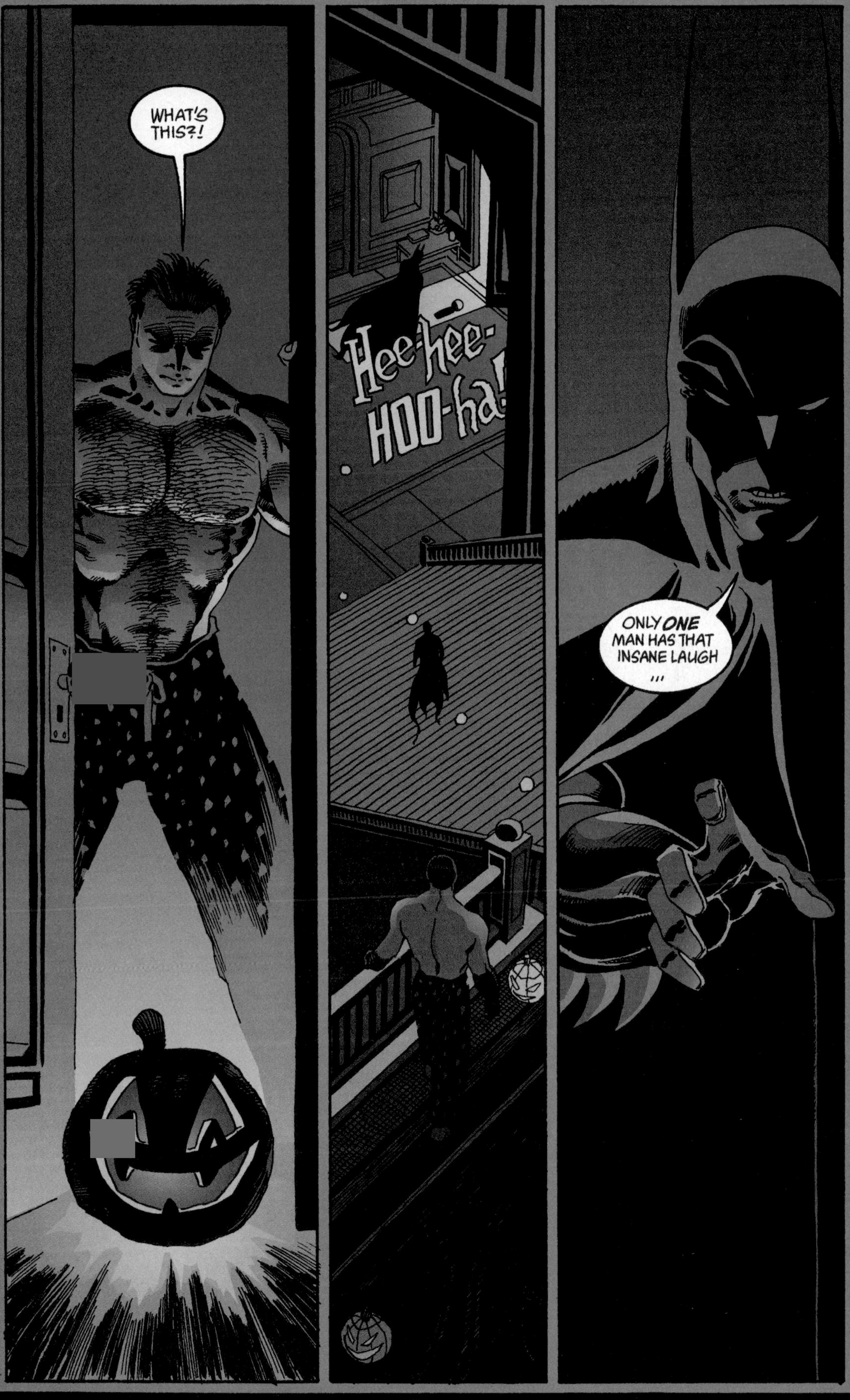

WHAT'S THIS?!

Joker. Joker. JOKER!

HEE-HOO-ha-ha-haa--HEEEEee--
hwa-ha ha ha ho ho ho hoo-ho hwa hoo hoo haaaa
heh.

OOO.
ROUGH-HOUSING.
MISSED ME.
MISSED ME.
NOW YOU GOTTA KISS ME.
YOU KNOW, FOR THE "WORLD'S GREATEST DETECTIVE"--
--YOU SURE ARE HAVING TROUBLE GETTING IT THROUGH YOUR THICK SKULL THAT YOU CAN'T TOUCH ME.
I MEAN, NO POINT IN BEATING A DEAD HORSE, BATTY, OLD BOY.
UNLESS, OF COURSE, YOU LIKE THE TASTE OF HORSE MEAT.
Another one of those...
...spirits?

Outside the house.
This nightmare... continues...
THIRD FLOOR. EVERYBODY OUT.
GARDEN SUPPLIES. LADIES' UNDER-GARMENTS.
AND OUR HALLOWEEN SHOWROOM.
THESE CHILDREN LIVE IN THE NEIGHBORHOOD.
WHAT POSSIBLE CONNECTION COULD THEY HAVE TO ME?
WHAT'RYA SCARED?
AM NOT.
ARE TOO
AM NOT.
WILL YOU TWO SHUT UP?!
H-HERE WE ARE...
WHO WOULD WANNA LIVE IN A PLACE LIKE THIS...?
THE GUY NEVER COMES OUT.
MY DAD TOLD ME THE HOUSE IS...
...HAUNTED!
YIKES!
LET'S GET OUTTA HERE!
AND THEY SAY CRIMINALS ARE A "SUPERSTITIOUS, COWARDLY LOT."
heh.

YA KNOW...
COME TO THINK OF IT.
NEITHER ONE OF US HAS ANY FRIENDS.
AND ANYBODY WHO WOULD WANT TO GET TO KNOW US WOULD HAVE TO BE--

NUTS!
I AM NOT.
IN ANY WAY.
LIKE YOU.

OH, NO?
...IDJA GET A GOOD GANDER AT THOSE KIDS' FACES?

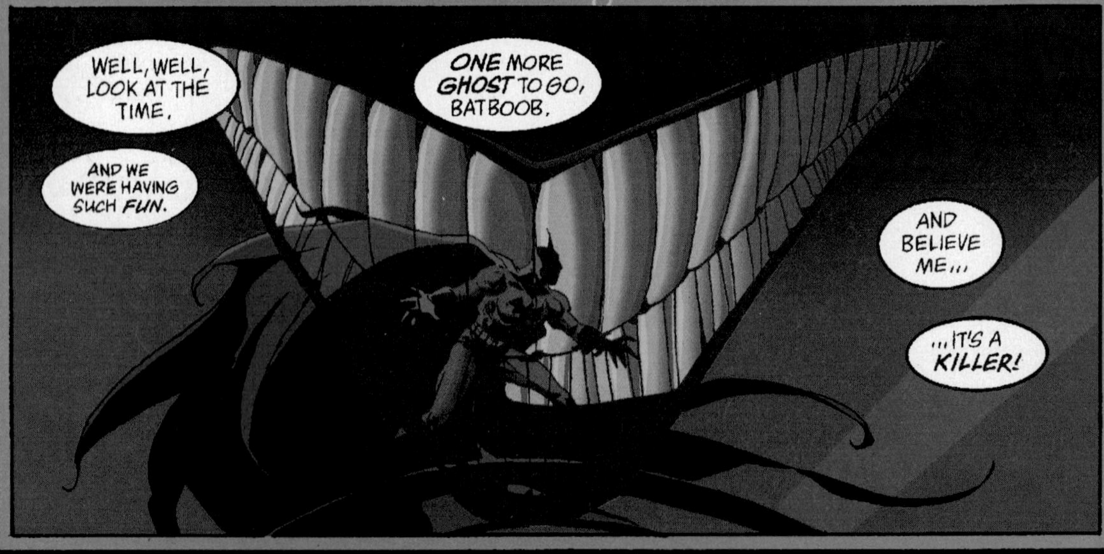
WELL, WELL, LOOK AT THE TIME.
AND WE WERE HAVING SUCH FUN.
ONE MORE GHOST TO GO, BATBOOB.
AND BELIEVE ME...
...IT'S A KILLER!

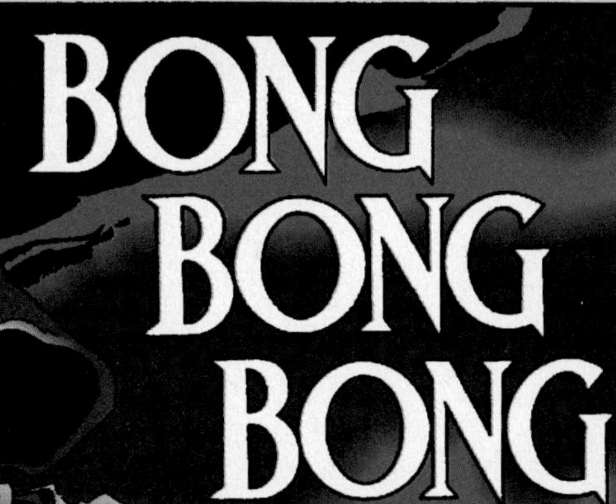
BONG
BONG
BONG

Cold.
KRAK
WHERE--
WHAT'S HAPPENED TO THE HOUSE?!
WHERE IS ALFRED?!
KRAK

I... KNOW THIS PLACE.
MY PARENTS ARE BURIED HERE.
WHO IS THAT DOWN THERE?
ALFRED...?
ONLY... MUCH OLDER AND...
...WHOSE LONELY GRAVE IS HE VISITING?

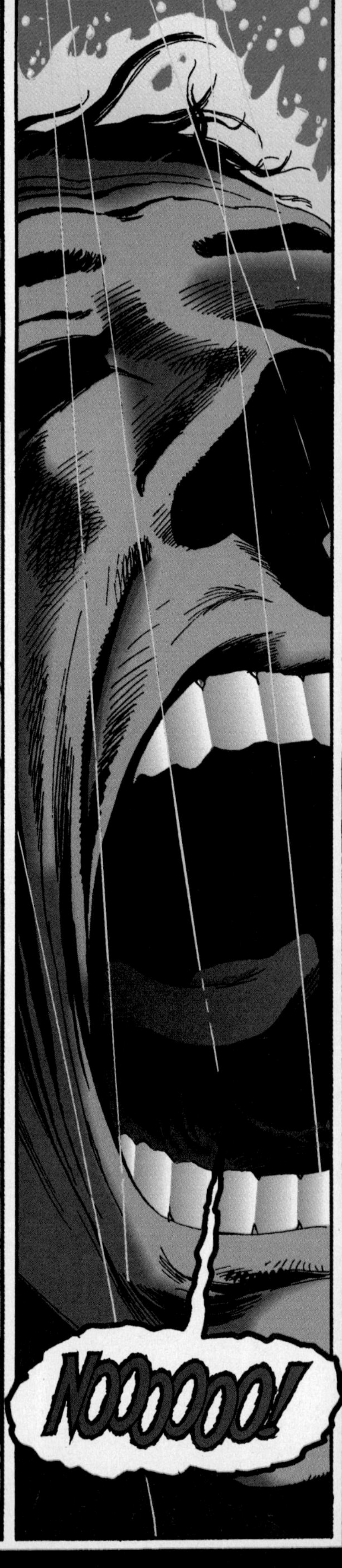
NOOOOOO!

HOW?
HOW DID THIS HAPPEN?
HOW WAS I SO EASILY FORGOTTEN?

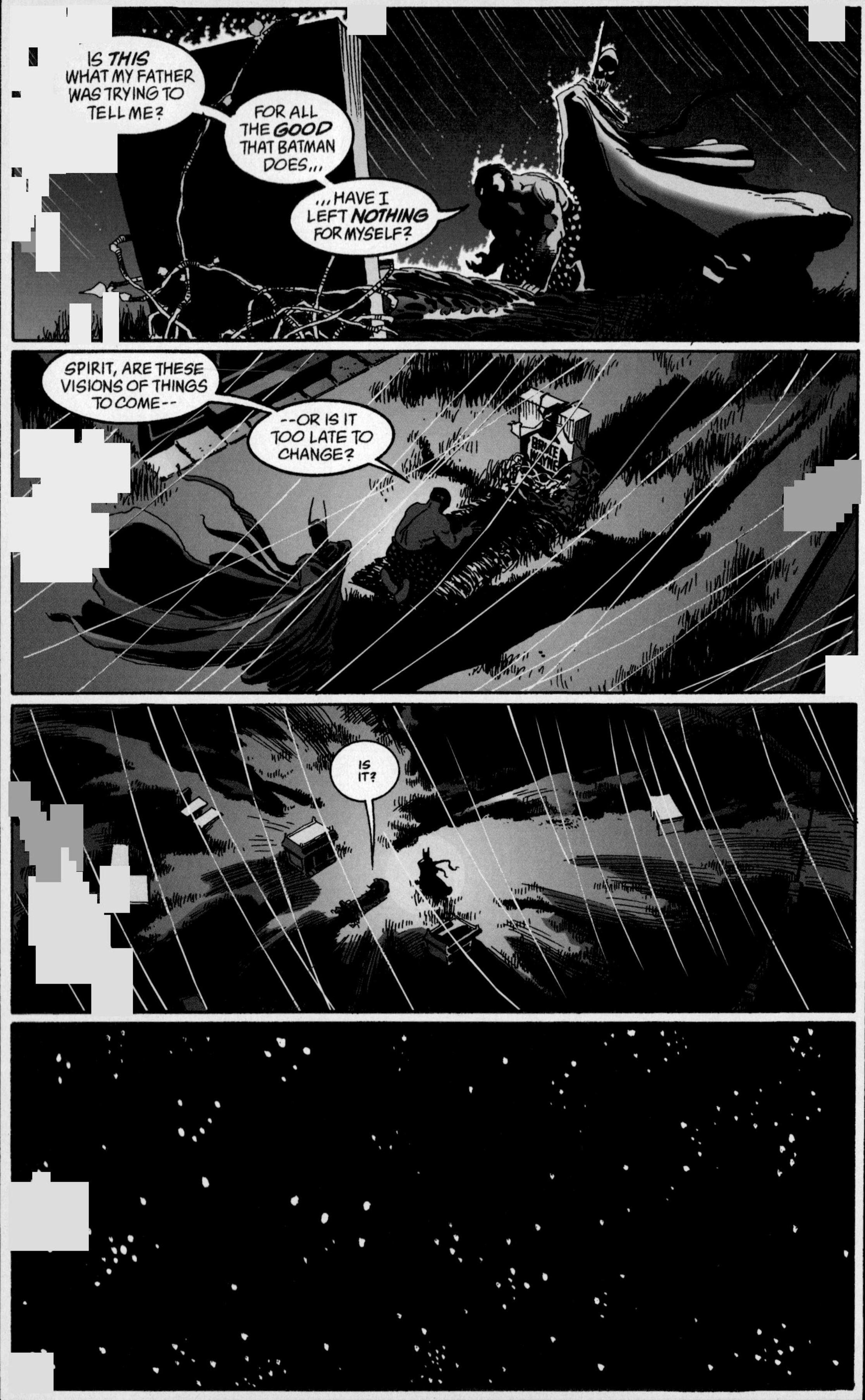
IS THIS WHAT MY FATHER WAS TRYING TO TELL ME?
FOR ALL THE GOOD THAT BATMAN DOES...
...HAVE I LEFT NOTHING FOR MYSELF?
SPIRIT, ARE THESE VISIONS OF THINGS TO COME--
--OR IS IT TOO LATE TO CHANGE?
IS IT?

SPIRIT?
SPIRIT...
YES, I SLEPT QUITE WELL, THANK YOU.
IT WAS YOU WHO WENT TO BED COMPLAINING OF HAVING EATEN SOMETHING--
--"THAT DIDN'T AGREE WITH YOU."
ALFRED!
WHAT IS THAT YOU'RE SAYING, SIR?
YOU'RE ALL RIGHT THEN!
GOTHAM
PENGUIN CAPTURED BY BATMAN
I'VE BROUGHT YOU TEA.
PLAIN TOAST.
AND AN ACCOUNT OF YET ANOTHER OF BATMAN'S THRILLING EXPLOITS.
WHAT DAY IS IT?
TODAY? WHY, IT'S HALLOWEEN, MASTER BRUCE.
TONIGHT WILL BE FRAUGHT WITH ALL SORTS OF CRIMINAL AC-TIVITY.
I ASSUME YOU'LL WANT YOUR COSTUME PRESSED.
ALFRED,
DO NOT ASSUME ANYTHING!
All in one night.

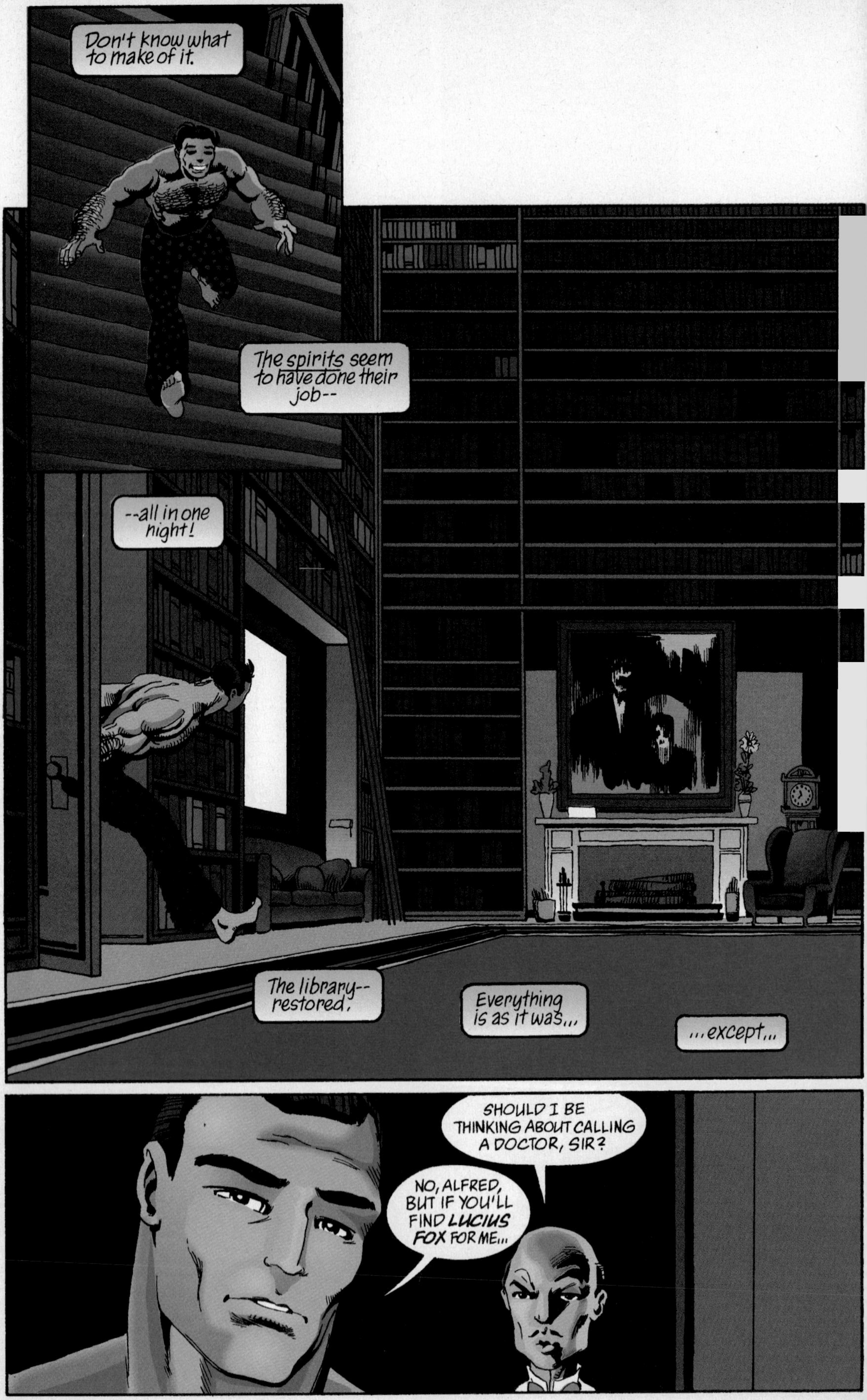

Don't know what to make of it.

The spirits seem to have done their job--

--all in one night!

The library--restored.

Everything is as it was...

...except...

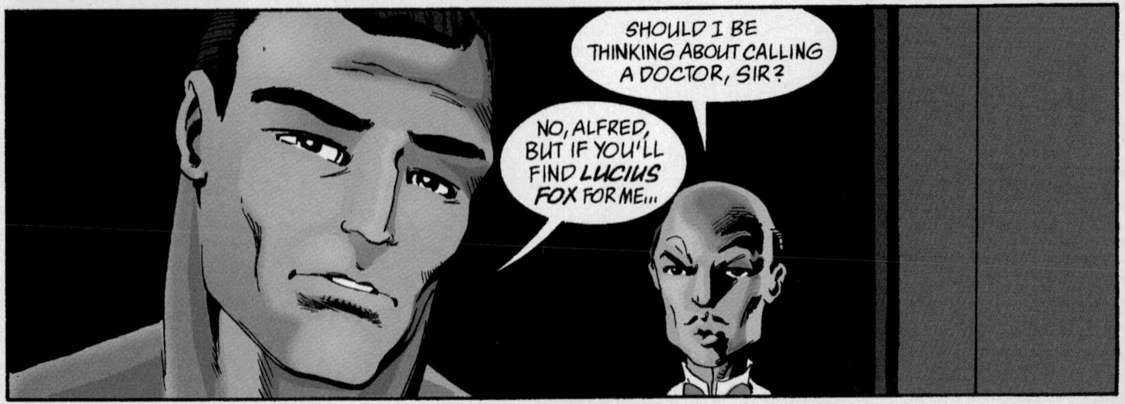

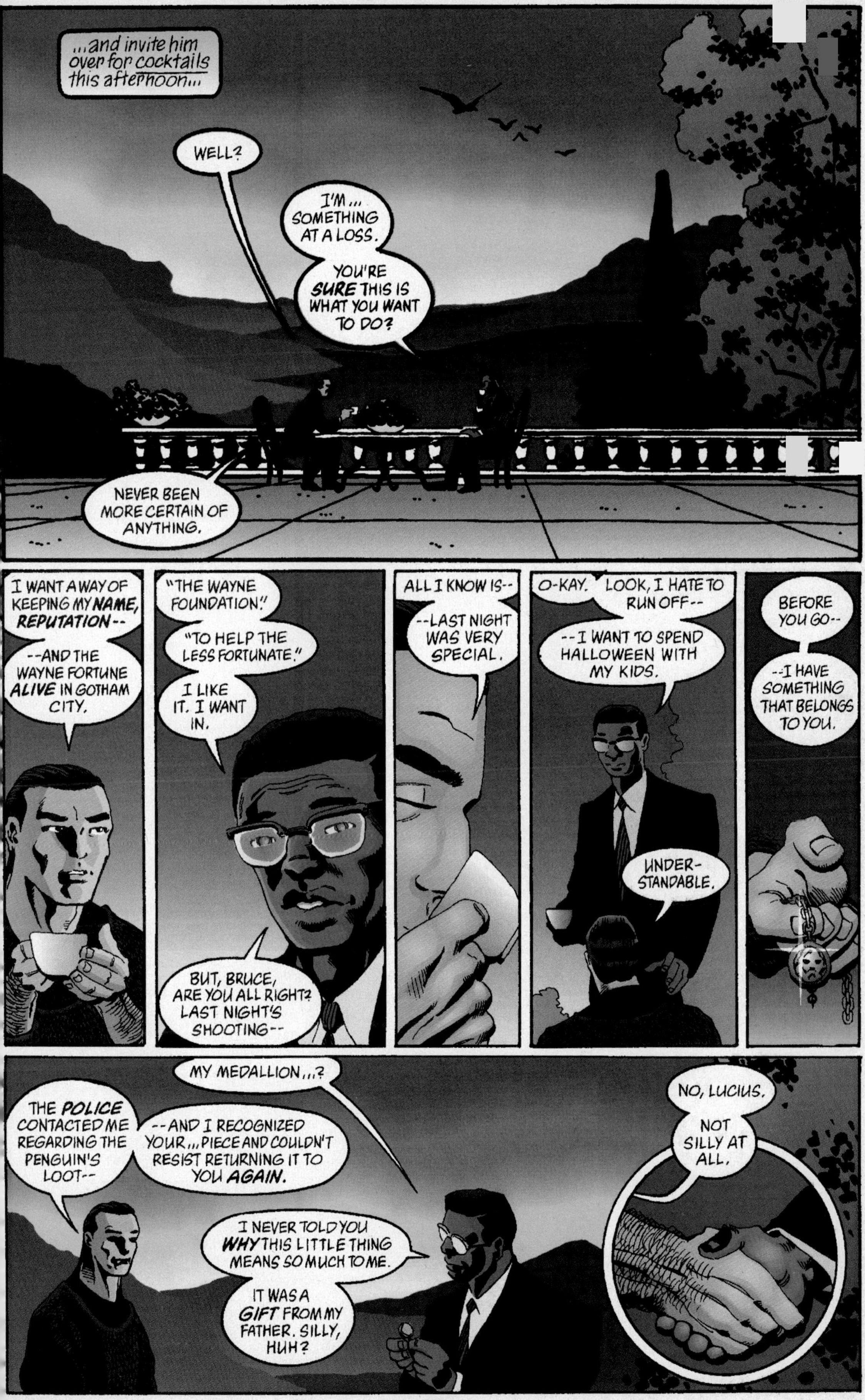

...and invite him over for cocktails this afternoon...

WELL?

I'M... SOMETHING AT A LOSS.

YOU'RE **SURE** THIS IS WHAT YOU WANT TO DO?

NEVER BEEN MORE CERTAIN OF ANYTHING.

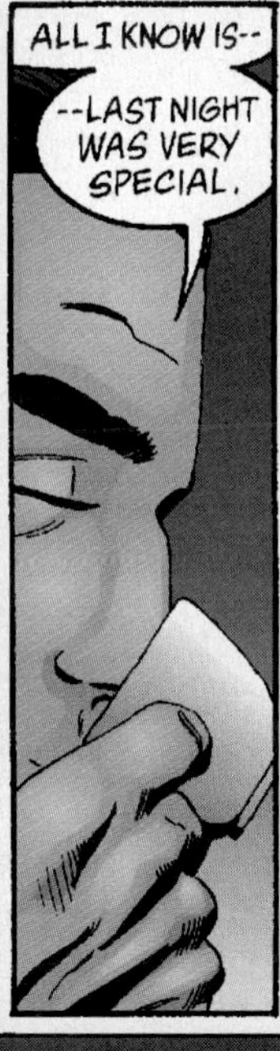

WOULDN'T YOU FEEL MORE COMFORTABLE GOING OUT THIS EVENING, SIR?
WHATEVER HAPPENS IN THE CITY TONIGHT, ALFRED, CAPTAIN GORDON AND HIS MEN CAN HANDLE IT.
I DARE SAY. I HOPE WE CAN AFFORD THE ELECTRIC BILL...
... I SCARCELY REMEMBER A TIME WHEN WE'VE HAD THIS MANY LIGHTS ON.
COOL...
TRICK OR TREAT!
HELLO.
I'll never truly understand what happened to me last night.
What's more, I'm not certain I want to.
Clearly, something had to be changed in my life.
And now... something has...
LOEB SALE 1995

JEPH LOEB is a screenwriter/producer living in Los Angeles. His current comic-book credits include *Wolverine/Gambit: Victims*, *X-Man*, *Cable*, and *X-Force* for Marvel as well as THE CHALLENGERS OF THE UNKNOWN and LOOSE CANNON for DC.

This one is dedicated to Tim Sale, the best pal a boy could have; and to the magic that is Archie Goodwin.

TIM SALE lives with his two dogs in the Northwest. His previous credits include *Wolverine/Gambit* for Marvel, *Deathblow* for Image, and *Grendel* for Dark Horse.

For Jeph, who on this Halloween run has given me the most fun I've ever had in comics. And for Archie, who let him.

GREG WRIGHT is not only an award-winning colorist but a prolific writer as well. Recent coloring credits include BATMAN, STARMAN, SUPERMAN/DOOMSDAY: HUNTER/PREY and SUPERMAN/ALIENS. Writing credits include *Silver Sable*, *Daredevil* and *Cosmic Powers*.

TODD KLEIN is a winner of Harvey and Eisner awards for his lettering. His work includes SANDMAN, BATMAN, *the Shadow*, and the graphic novel *Starstruck*.

THE QUEST FOR JUSTICE CONTINUES IN THESE BOOKS FROM TITAN:

BATMAN: ARKHAM ASYLUM
Grant Morrison • Dave McKean
ISBN: 1 85286 280 7

BATMAN: BLOODSTORM
Doug Moench • Kelley Jones • John Beatty
ISBN: 1 85286 610 1

BATMAN: CASTLE OF THE BAT
Jack C. Harris • Bo Hampton
ISBN: 1 85286 605 5

BATMAN: COLLECTED LEGENDS OF THE DARK KNIGHT
James Robinson • Alan Grant • Various
ISBN: 1 85286 572 X

BATMAN: CONTAGION
Various
ISBN: 1 85286 732 9

BATMAN: DARK JOKER - THE WILD
Doug Moench • Kelley Jones • John Beatty
ISBN: 1 85286 580 6

BATMAN: THE DARK KNIGHT RETURNS
Frank Miller
ISBN: 1 85286 090 0

BATMAN: DARK LEGENDS
Dennis O'Neil • Bryan Talbot • Various
ISBN: 1 85286 723 X

BATMAN: A DEATH IN THE FAMILY
Jim Starlin • Jim Aparo • Mike DeCarlo
ISBN: 1 85286 207 6

BATMAN & DRACULA: RED RAIN
Doug Moench • Kelley Jones
ISBN: 1 85286 437 0

BATMAN: FACES
Matt Wagner
ISBN: 1 85286 528 8

BATMAN: FEATURING TWO-FACE AND THE RIDDLER
Bob Kane • Neil Gaiman • Various
ISBN: 1 85286 654 3

BATMAN: HAUNTED KNIGHT
Jeph Loeb • Tim Sale
ISBN: 1 85286 739 6

BATMAN: THE KILLING JOKE
Alan Moore • Brian Bolland • John Higgins
ISBN: 1 85286 082 0

BATMAN KNIGHTFALL: PT1 - BROKEN BAT
Doug Moench • Various
ISBN: 1 85286 515 6

BATMAN KNIGHTFALL: PT2 - WHO RULES THE NIGHT?
Doug Moench • Various
ISBN: 1 85286 516 4

BATMAN: KNIGHTSEND
Chuck Dixon • Alan Grant • Various
ISBN: 1 85286 614 4

BATMAN: THE LAST ANGEL
Eric Van Lustbader • Lee Moder • Scott Hanna
ISBN: 1 85286 582 2

BATMAN: THE LAST ARKHAM
Alan Grant • Norm Breyfogle
ISBN: 1 85286 665 9

BATMAN: SWORD OF AZRAEL
Dennis O'Neil • Joe Quesada • Kevin Nowlan
ISBN: 1 85286 496 6

BATMAN VS PREDATOR
Dave Gibbons • Andy Kubert • Adam Kubert
ISBN: 1 85286 446 X

BATMAN VS PREDATOR II: BLOODMATCH
Doug Moench • Paul Gulacy • Terry Austin
ISBN: 1 85286 667 5

SUPERMAN/BATMAN: ALTERNATE HISTORIES
John Byrne • Various
ISBN: 1 85286 715 9

SUPERMAN/BATMAN: ALTERNATE DESTINIES
Karl Kesel • Various
ISBN: 1 85286 738 8

SUPERMAN/BATMAN: WORLD'S FINEST
Dave Gibbons • Steve Rude • Karl Kesel
ISBN: 1 85286 438 9

BATMAN: THE COLLECTED ADVENTURES - VOL
Kelley Puckett • Martin Pasko • Ty Templeton
ISBN: 1 85286 521 0

BATMAN: THE COLLECTED ADVENTURES - VOL
Kelley Puckett • Mike Parobeck • Rick Burchett
ISBN: 1 85286 563 6

All *Batman* publications are available through most good bookshops or direct from our mail order service.
To order telephone 01536 763 631 with your credit card details or contact Titan Books Mail Order, PO Box 54, Desborough, Northants., NN14 2UH, quoting reference BHK/GN.